FIRST PAST THE POST® SERI

11+ NUMERICAL REASONING

Short Numerical Reasoning

Book 1

Tests 1 - 10

How to use this pack to make the most of 11+ exam preparation

It is important to remember that for 11+ exams there is no national syllabus, no pass mark and no retake option! It is therefore vitally important that your child is fully primed in order so that perform to the best of their ability and give themselves the best possible chance on the day.

Unlike similar publications, the **First Past the Post®** series uniquely assesses your child's performance on a question-by-question basis, helping to identify areas for improvement and providing suggestions for further targeted tests.

Numerical Reasoning

This series of tests is representative of the short numerical reasoning section of contemporary multi-discipline 11+ tests, which typically have two papers. One paper usually has a section of long worded numerical reasoning problems and the other contains short, quick fire questions more akin to traditional maths. This publication addresses the latter. The suggested time for each paper is provided based on classroom testing sessions held at our centre.

Never has it been more useful to learn from mistakes!

Students can improve by as much as 15 percent not only by focused practice, but also by targeting any weak areas.

How to manage your child's own practice

To access the most up-to-date information, log on to the ElevenPlusExams website (www.elevenplusexams.co.uk). ElevenPlusExams is the largest UK on-line resource with over 40,000 webpages and a forum administered by a select group of experienced moderators.

About the authors

The ElevenPlusExams **First Past the Post®** series has been created by a team of experienced tutors and authors from leading British universities including Oxford and Cambridge.

Published by University of Buckingham Press

With special thanks to the children who tested our material at the ElevenPlusExams centre in Harrow.

ISBN: 9781908684431

Contents Page

This workbook comprises ten tests, made up of twenty short questions each. Each should take six minutes to complete.

Once you have completed each test, mark it using the answers and explanations provided and upload it onto our 11+ Peer Compare System™. This allows you to see how well you performed in comparison to others who have taken the same test.

You can register by visiting www.ElevenPlusExams.co.uk/FirstPastThePost to post your results anonymously and obtain the feedback.

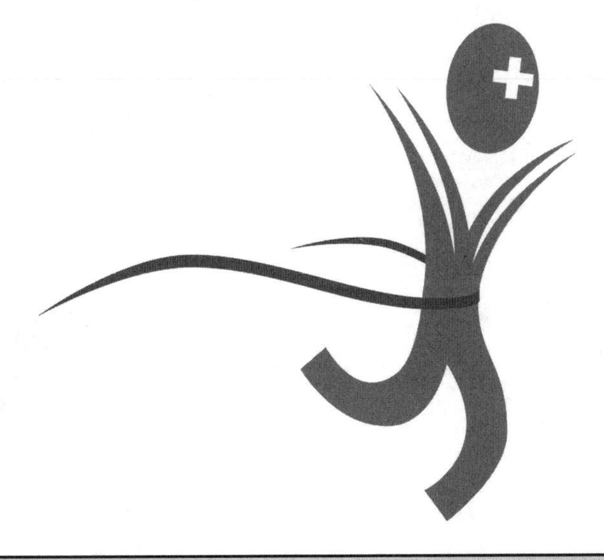

Instructions

In this book there are boxes given to you in which to write your answers, such as the one below:

Place value is determined by which box you choose to write your numbers in, for example the correct ways to write '10' and '7.65' are shown below:

If the answer is a negative value, use one of the answer boxes to write a negative sign as shown below:

Some questions are multiple choice, when this is the case there will be a box underneath each answer for you to mark your answer in. The correct way to do so is with a line through the box, as shown below; **do not** circle it.

FIRST PAST THE POST® SERIES

Short Numerical Reasoning

Test 1

Read the following instructions carefully:

1. You have 6 minutes to complete this test of 20 questions.
2. Work as quickly and carefully as you can.
3. When you have finished a page, go straight onto the next page until you finish the test.
4. You can use all the available space around the question to do your working; however, only write the answer in the answer boxes.
5. To change an answer, rub out your original answer and note down the new answer, aligning it to any answer boxes.
6. If you cannot answer a question, go on to the next question.
7. When you have completed this paper go back to any questions you have missed out and check your answers.
8. Calculators and protractors are not permitted in this test.

Good luck!

After you have finished this paper you can use the 11+ Peer Compare System™ to see how well you performed compared to others who have taken this test. You can register by visiting www.ElevenPlusExams.co.uk/FirstPastThePost to post your results anonymously and obtain the feedback.

Total	**/ 20**

Question 1

A number machine has an output of 65 and an operation of '× 5'. What is the input?

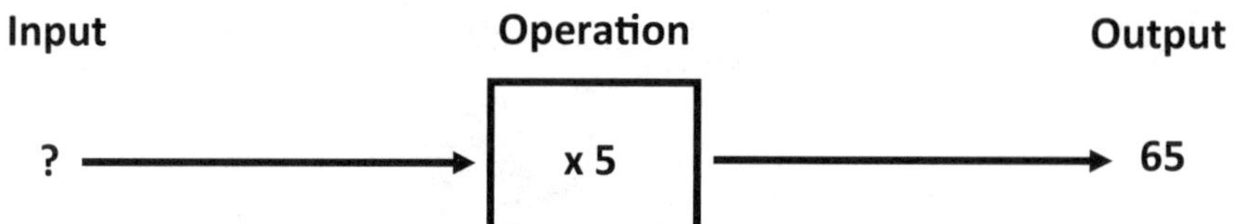

Question 2

If $x + 14 = 21$, what would be the value of x?

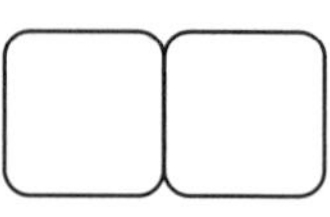

Question 3

Find the mean of the set of numbers below.

7 5 17 12 15 4

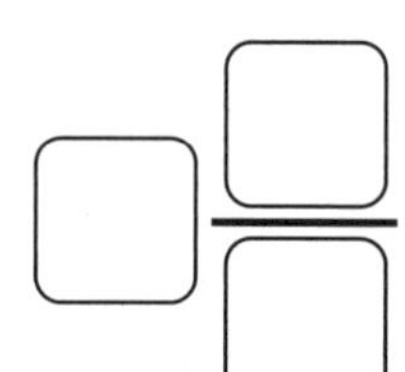

Question 4

Write $^{67}/_9$ as a mixed number.

Question 5

What is the volume of the cuboid below?

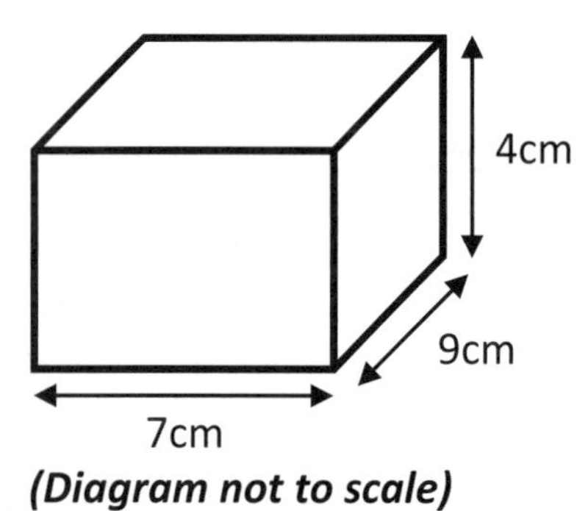

(Diagram not to scale)

cm³

Question 6

What is the area of a square which has sides of length 16cm?

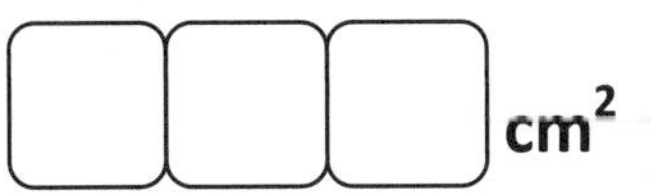

Question 7

In a class there are 14 boys and 18 girls. What is the ratio of boys to girls in the class?

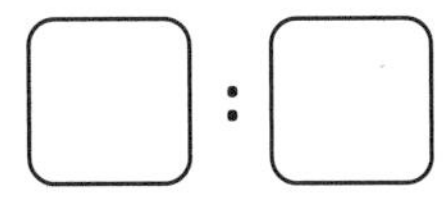

Question 8

You are facing NE and turn 135° anticlockwise, which direction are you now facing? Use the compass below to help you.

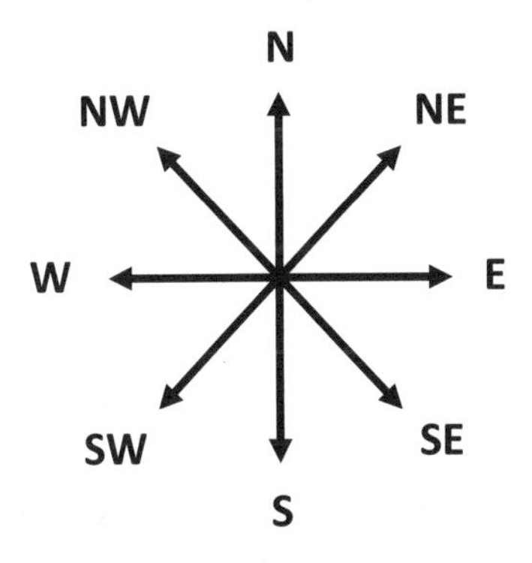

Question 9

What is $(12 - 5) + 1 - 2^2 + 5$?

Question 10

How many sides does a pentagon have?

Question 11

How would 3.45pm be displayed on a 24-hour clock?

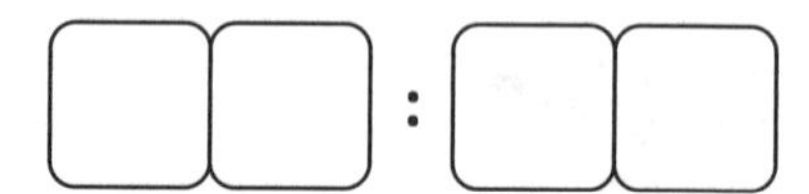

Question 12

What is the value of the 3 in 513000?

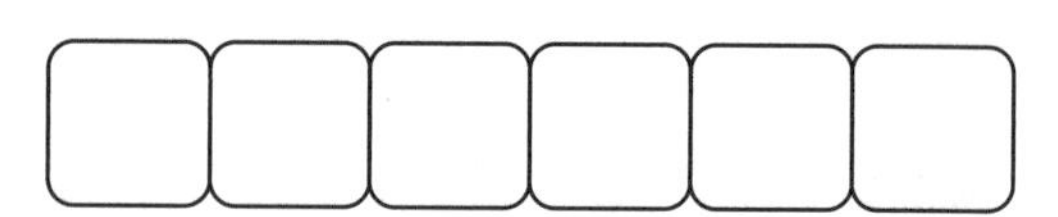

Question 13

What is the difference in area between the rectangle and triangle shown below?

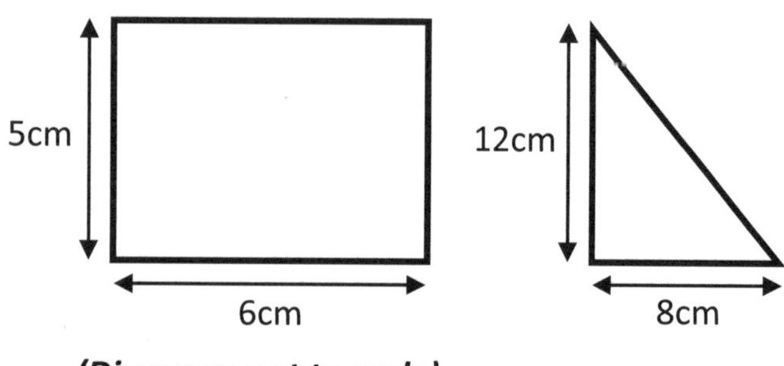

(Diagrams not to scale)

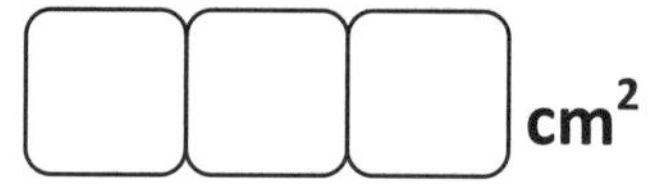

Question 14

Convert 1325 centimetres into metres.

Question 15

If this pentagonal prism has a length of 11cm and its pentagonal face has an area of 25cm^2, what is its volume?

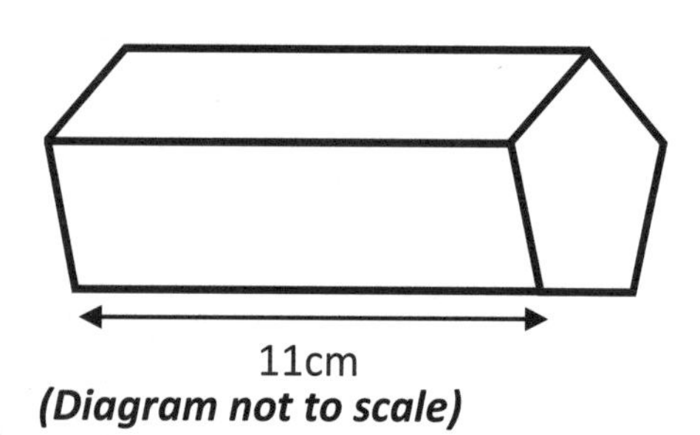

(Diagram not to scale)

cm^3

Question 16

The centre of a circle has the coordinates (-5,8). What are the new coordinates of the centre when it is translated 5 units to the right and 2 units up?

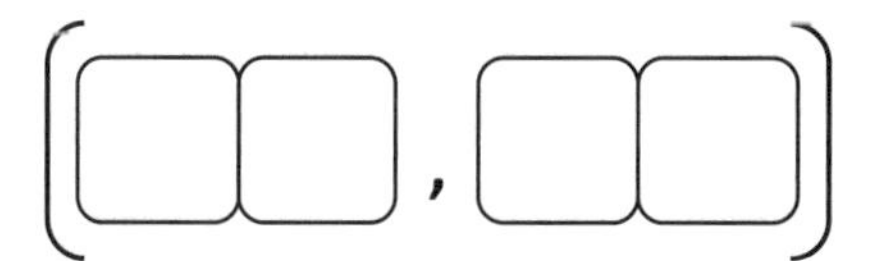

Question 17

How much water is in this container?

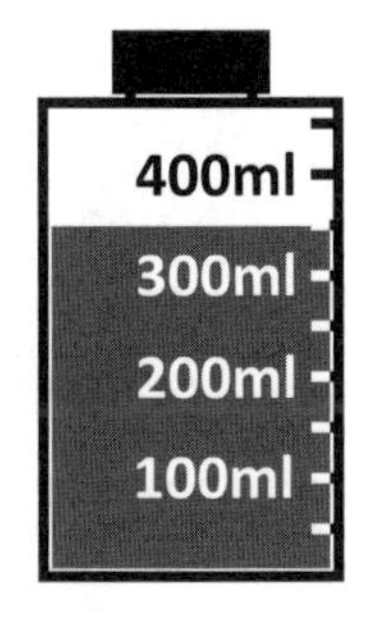

ml

Question 18

What is the order of rotational symmetry of a rectangle?

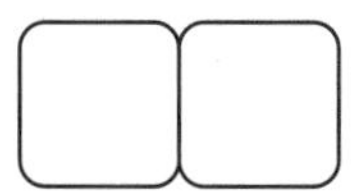

Question 19

How many edges does a triangular prism have?

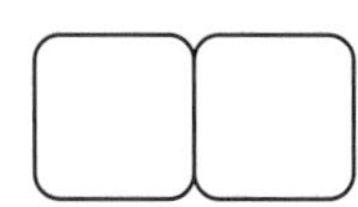

Question 20

1200 students were asked what their favourite sport was and the results were displayed in the pie chart below. How many students chose swimming as their favourite sport?

Favourite Sport of Students

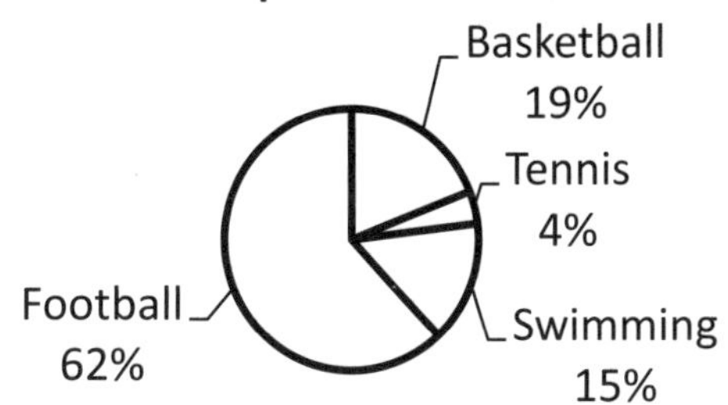

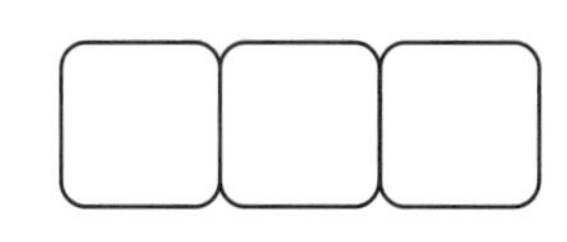

BLANK PAGE

Short Numerical Reasoning

Test 2

Read the following instructions carefully:

1. You have 6 minutes to complete this test of 20 questions.
2. Work as quickly and carefully as you can.
3. When you have finished a page, go straight onto the next page until you finish the test.
4. You can use all the available space around the question to do your working; however, only write the answer in the answer boxes.
5. To change an answer, rub out your original answer and note down the new answer, aligning it to any answer boxes.
6. If you cannot answer a question, go on to the next question.
7. When you have completed this paper go back to any questions you have missed out and check your answers.
8. Calculators and protractors are not permitted in this test.

Good luck!

After you have finished this paper you can use the 11+ Peer Compare System™ to see how well you performed compared to others who have taken this test. You can register by visiting www.ElevenPlusExams.co.uk/FirstPastThePost to post your results anonymously and obtain the feedback.

Total	**/ 20**

Question 1

What is the perimeter of the rectangle below?

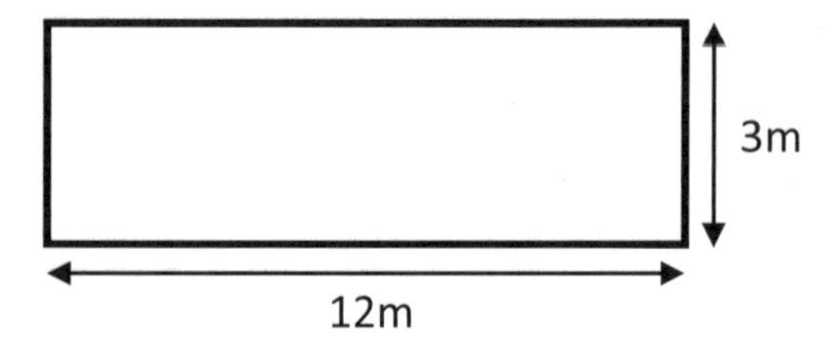

(Diagram not to scale)

Question 2

How many faces does a hexagonal prism have?

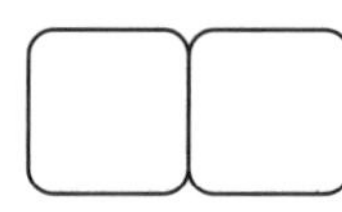

Question 3

Calculate the volume of the triangular prism shown below.

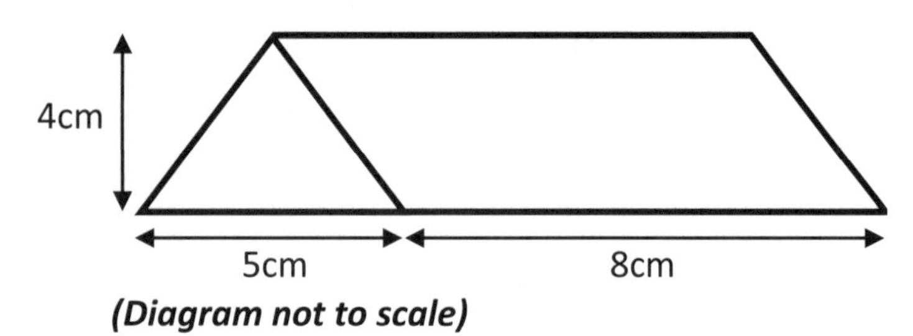

(Diagram not to scale)

Question 4

How many pairs of parallel faces does a cuboid have?

Question 5

A number machine has an output of 13 and an operation of '- 59'. What is the input?

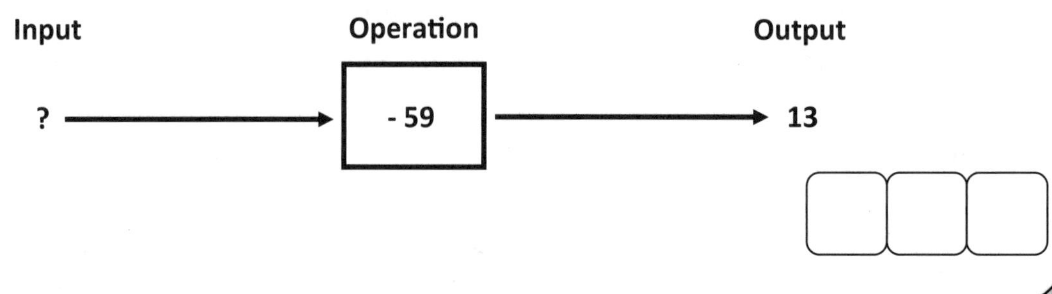

Question 6

Is 108° a reflex, obtuse or acute angle? Mark your answer below.

Reflex **Obtuse** **Acute**

Question 7

What is the probability of picking an ace at random from a complete deck of 52 cards?

Question 8

What is the value of the 7 in 3478?

Question 9

How many times does 9 go into 387?

Question 10

A rectangle has the coordinates: (2,5), (2,2) and (7,2). What is the fourth coordinate?

Question 11

Which type of triangle has the most lines of symmetry? Mark your answer below.

Equilateral **Isosceles** **Scalene**

Question 12

A train leaves Leeds at 09:30 and takes 210 minutes to reach London. What time does the train reach London? Give your answer in the 24-hour clock format.

:

Question 13

How many vertices does a kite have?

Question 14

A cylinder has a cross sectional area of $32cm^2$ and a volume of $192cm^3$. Work out the length of the cylinder.

cm

Question 15

How many of the numbers below are prime?

31 **2** **1** **41** **10** **25**

Question 16

Express 4 $^{3}/_{10}$ as a top heavy fraction.

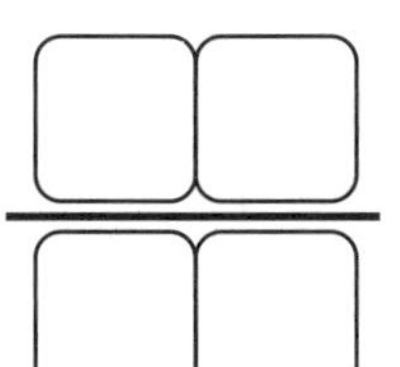

Question 17

What is the missing number in the sequence shown below?

	13	20	27	34	41

Question 18

What is the perimeter of a square with sides of length 12m?

Question 19

What is the missing number in the sequence shown below?

56	58	62	68	76	

Question 20

James scored 34 out of 50 on his science test. What is this as a percentage?

BLANK PAGE

Short Numerical Reasoning

Test 3

Read the following instructions carefully:

1. You have 6 minutes to complete this test of 20 questions.
2. Work as quickly and carefully as you can.
3. When you have finished a page, go straight onto the next page until you finish the test.
4. You can use all the available space around the question to do your working; however, only write the answer in the answer boxes.
5. To change an answer, rub out your original answer and note down the new answer, aligning it to any answer boxes.
6. If you cannot answer a question, go on to the next question.
7. When you have completed this paper go back to any questions you have missed out and check your answers.
8. Calculators and protractors are not permitted in this test.

Good luck!

After you have finished this paper you can use the 11+ Peer Compare System™ to see how well you performed compared to others who have taken this test. You can register by visiting www.ElevenPlusExams.co.uk/FirstPastThePost to post your results anonymously and obtain the feedback.

Total	**/ 20**

Question 1

What is the product of 8, 12 and 20?

Question 2

If 5th September is a Thursday, on what day of the week would the 19th September fall in that same year? Mark your answer below.

Monday	Tuesday	Wednesday	Thursday	Friday	Saturday	Sunday
⬭	⬭	⬭	⬭	⬭	⬭	⬭

Question 3

What is the sum of 5 squared and 3 cubed?

Question 4

If 282 marbles were to be divided equally amongst three friends, how many marbles would each of them have?

Question 5

Daniel and Ashley decide to meet in Harrow at 1.30pm. It takes Daniel 15 minutes less than Ashley to travel to Harrow. If Ashley takes 50 minutes to get to Harrow, at what time must Daniel leave his house in order to meet Ashley on time?

. pm

Question 6

A right-angle triangle has coordinates (4,1), (4,7) and (10,1). What is the area of this triangle?

Question 7

In a zoo there are 12 monkeys, 4 elephants and 6 zebras. What is the ratio of zebras to monkeys to elephants?

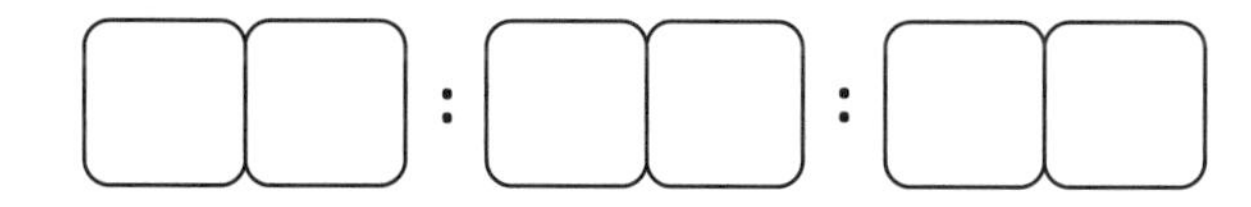

Question 8

Convert 0.52 kilometres into centimetres.

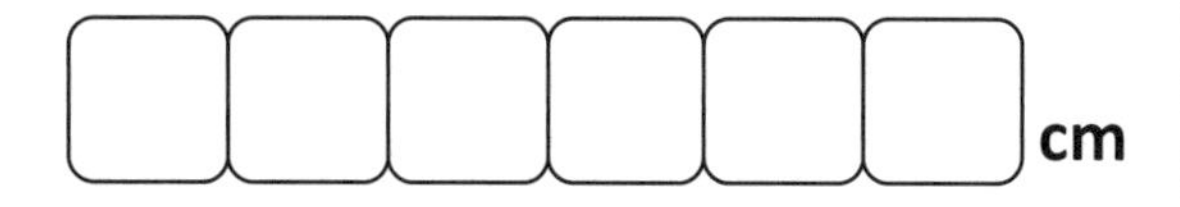

Question 9

A number machine has an output of 16 and an operation of '÷ 8'. What is the input?

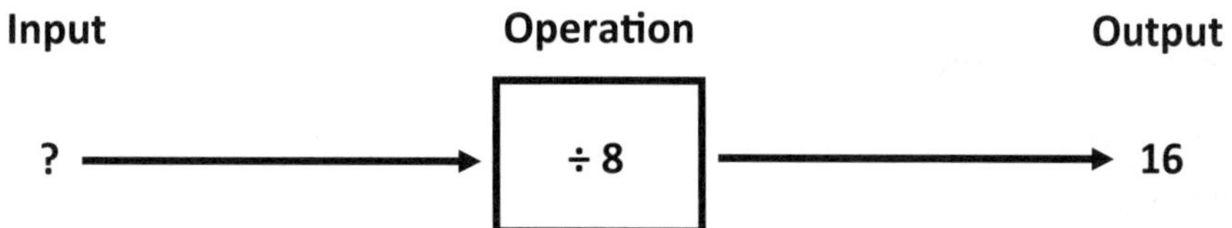

Question 10

How many edges does a triangular based pyramid have?

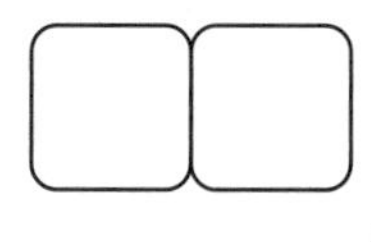

Question 11

What is the area of the triangle shown below?

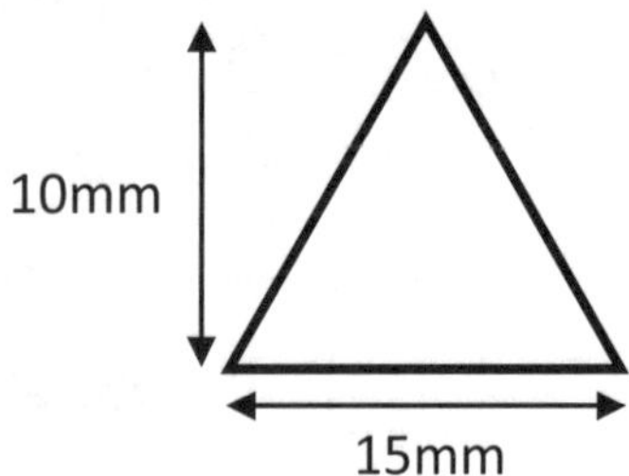

(Diagram not to scale)

Question 12

A triangle has two angles of 96° and 26°. What is the third angle?

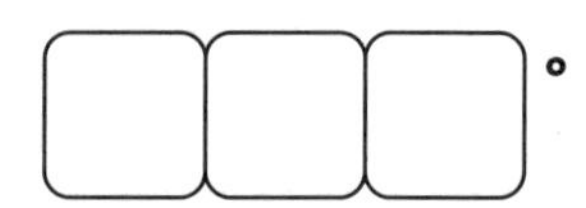

Question 13

Mary has £28, Robert has £19 and Raman has £34.50. How much money do they have in total?

Question 14

The number of cars of different colours at a local car dealer is represented by the bar chart below. How many cars are there in total?

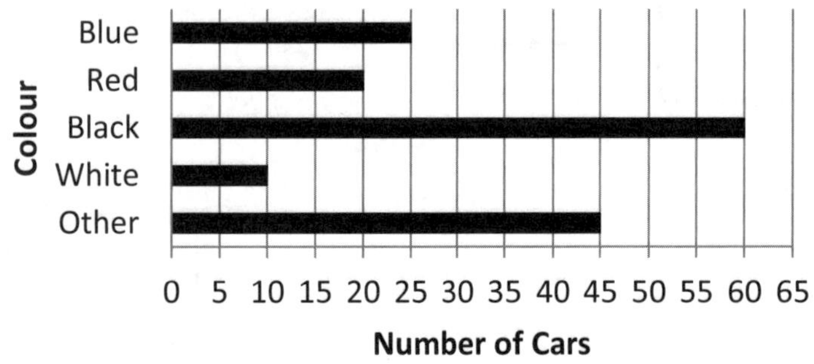

Question 15

What is the lowest common multiple of 8 and 12?

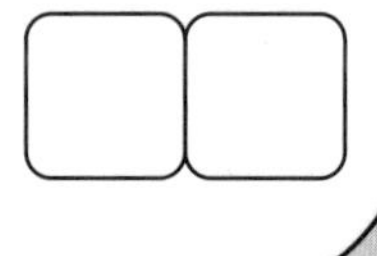

Question 16

The current temperature is -0.8°C. If the temperature rises by 2.5°C, what will the new temperature be?

Question 17

The average number of train delays per day was recorded over a week in the line chart below. Between which two days was there no change in the number of delays?

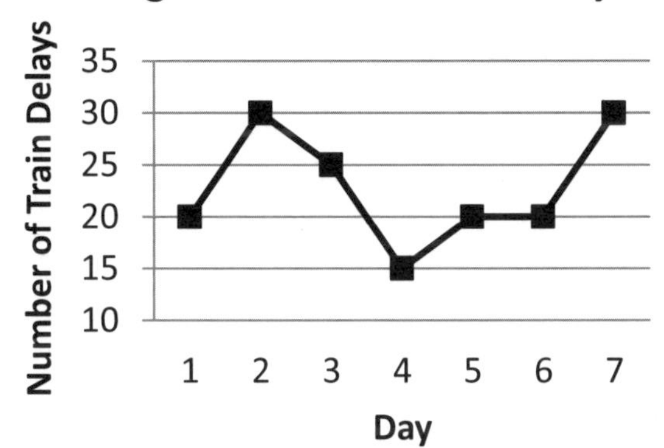

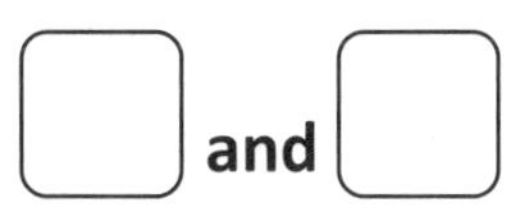

Question 18

If a right-angle triangle has an angle of 45°, what type of triangle is it? Mark your answer below.

Equilateral **Isosceles** **Scalene**

Question 19

If x - 9 = 32, what is the value of x?

Question 20

Point P has coordinates (3,-6). What would the new coordinates of point P be if it were reflected in the x-axis?

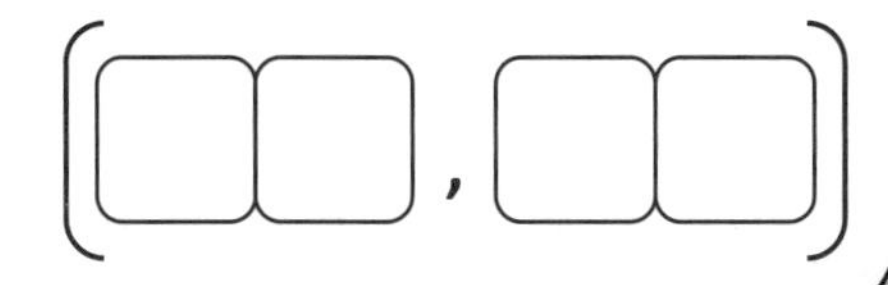

BLANK PAGE

Short Numerical Reasoning

Test 4

Read the following instructions carefully:

1. You have 6 minutes to complete this test of 20 questions.
2. Work as quickly and carefully as you can.
3. When you have finished a page, go straight onto the next page until you finish the test.
4. You can use all the available space around the question to do your working; however, only write the answer in the answer boxes.
5. To change an answer, rub out your original answer and note down the new answer, aligning it to any answer boxes.
6. If you cannot answer a question, go on to the next question.
7. When you have completed this paper go back to any questions you have missed out and check your answers.
8. Calculators and protractors are not permitted in this test.

Good luck!

After you have finished this paper you can use the 11+ Peer Compare System™ to see how well you performed compared to others who have taken this test. You can register by visiting www.ElevenPlusExams.co.uk/FirstPastThePost to post your results anonymously and obtain the feedback.

Total	**/ 20**

Question 1

Point A has coordinates (8,-4). If point A moves up 3 units and left 4 units, what are its new coordinates?

Question 2

What is the value of $54 + 36 - (2^3 - 1)$?

Question 3

What is the next triangular number after 10?

Question 4

What is the order of rotational symmetry of a square?

Question 5

How many of the smaller cubes fit into the larger cube?

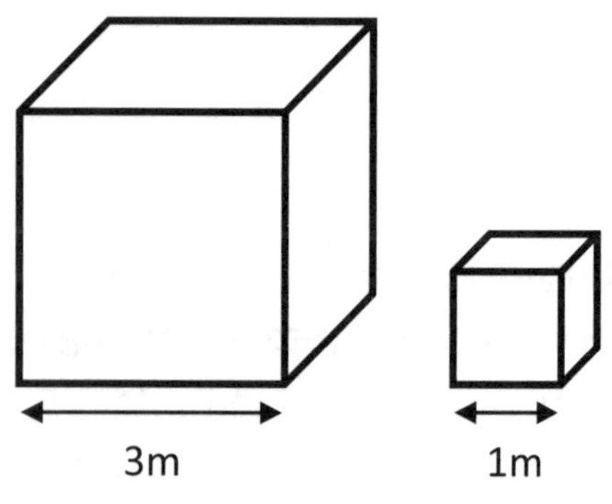

(Diagrams not to scale)

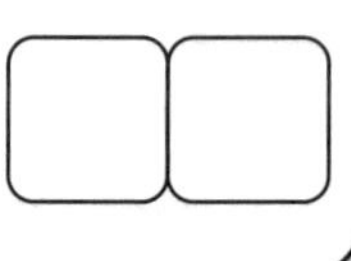

Question 6

What is the difference between the perimeters of the two shapes below?

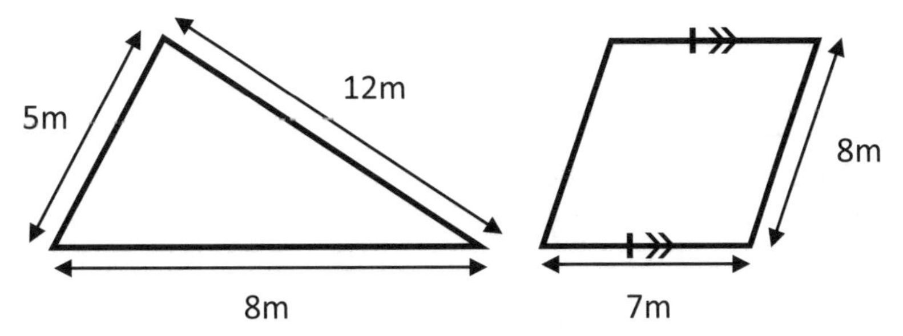

(Diagrams not to scale)

m

Question 7

A number machine has an output of 154 and an operation of '- 47'. What is the input?

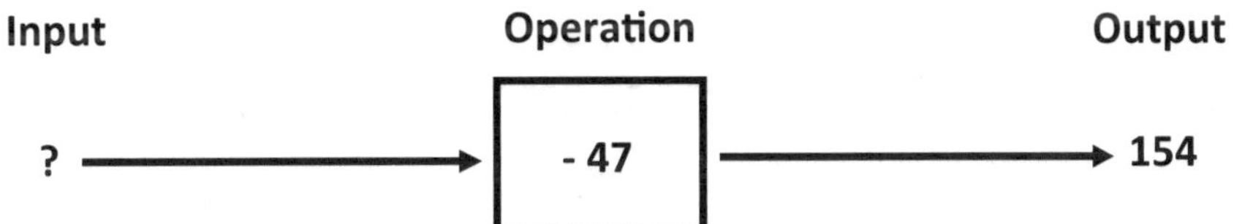

Question 8

How many vertices does a cube have?

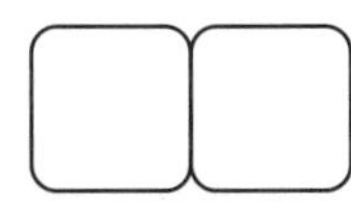

Question 9

Find the range of the set of numbers below.

18 16 15 22 34 7 11

Question 10

Which square number lies between 40 and 50?

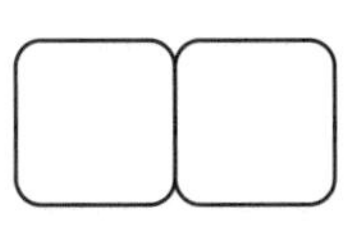

Question 11

Which of the options best describes the relationship between the lines below? Mark your answer below.

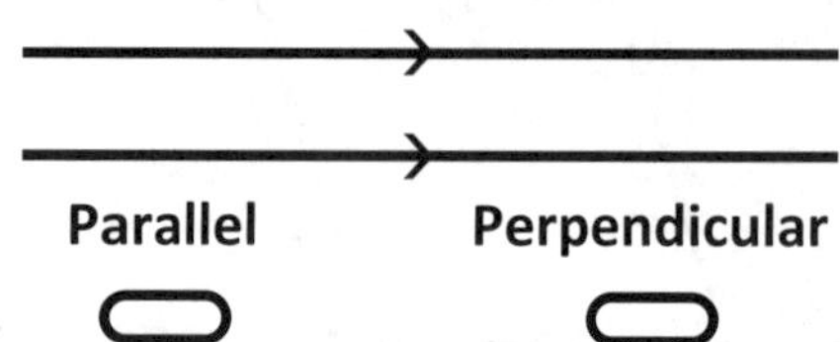

Parallel **Perpendicular**

Question 12

The amount of time taken for Liam to complete his homework is recorded over 25 days in a tally chart. Which is the modal group? Mark your answer below.

Time (minutes)	0-15	16-30	31-45	46-60	61-75
Tally	||||	卌 ||	卌 卌 |	||	|
Frequency	4	7	11	2	1

0-15 **16-30** **31-45** **46-60** **61-75**

Question 13

What is the sum of the first 3 multiples of 6 which are greater than 15?

Question 14

A point at (3,-3) is rotated 90° anticlockwise about the origin. What are the point's new coordinates?

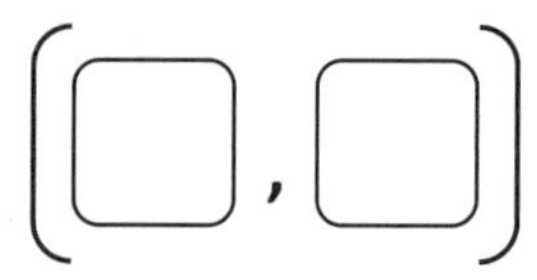

Question 15

Convert 8010 millimetres into metres.

Question 16

What is the area of a rectangle with sides of length 12cm and 10cm?

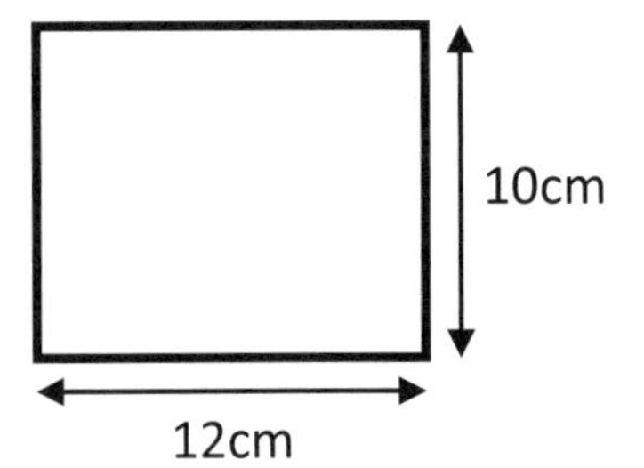

(Diagram not to scale)

Question 17

Mary is walking towards her school along a straight path. On what bearing is she walking? Use the compass below to help you.

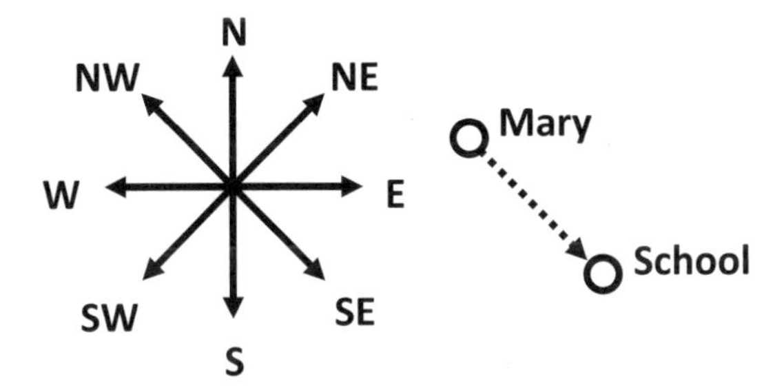

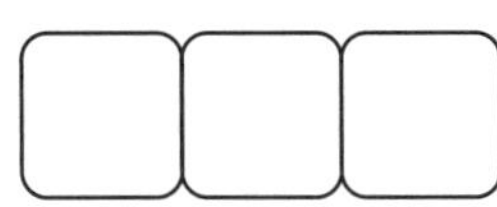

Question 18

In a car park there are 457 red cars and 264 black cars. What is the total number of red and black cars in the car park?

Question 19

Christian marked his height on a scale on a wall with a dashed line, as shown below. The next time he checked his height, he had grown by 5cm. How tall is he now?

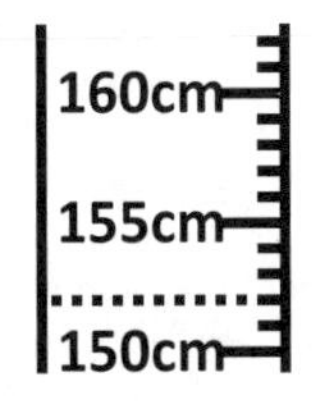

Question 20

In a pencil case there are 54 pencils and 12 pens. What is the ratio of pencils to pens?

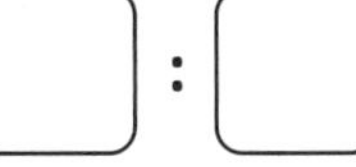

BLANK PAGE

FIRST PAST THE POST® SERIES

Short Numerical Reasoning

Test 5

Read the following instructions carefully:

1. You have 6 minutes to complete this test of 20 questions.
2. Work as quickly and carefully as you can.
3. When you have finished a page, go straight onto the next page until you finish the test.
4. You can use all the available space around the question to do your working; however, only write the answer in the answer boxes.
5. To change an answer, rub out your original answer and note down the new answer, aligning it to any answer boxes.
6. If you cannot answer a question, go on to the next question.
7. When you have completed this paper go back to any questions you have missed out and check your answers.
8. Calculators and protractors are not permitted in this test.

Good luck!

After you have finished this paper you can use the 11+ Peer Compare System™ to see how well you performed compared to others who have taken this test. You can register by visiting www.ElevenPlusExams.co.uk/FirstPastThePost to post your results anonymously and obtain the feedback.

Total	**/ 20**

Question 1

What is 0.07km + 18m + 26m?

Question 2

How many edges does a cube have?

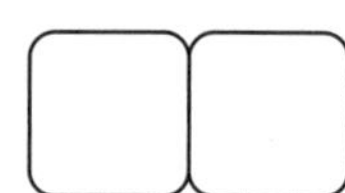

Question 3

Convert 4730 grams into kilograms.

Question 4

How many more lines of symmetry does a regular pentagon have compared with an isosceles triangle?

Question 5

The triangular prism below has a volume of $60cm^3$. The triangular face of the prism has an area of $6cm^2$. Work out the length (l) of the triangular prism.

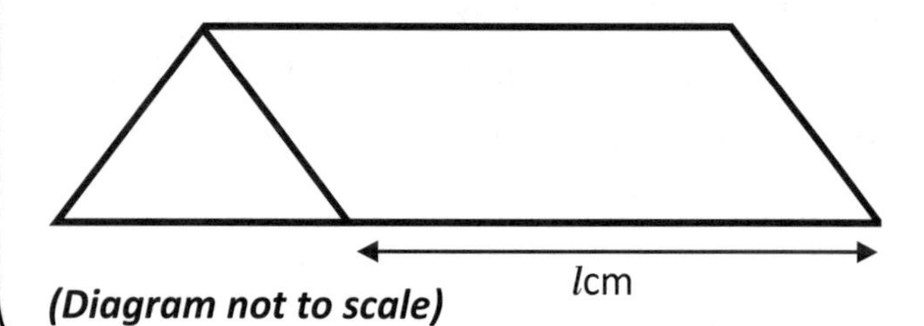

(Diagram not to scale)

cm

Question 6

If $6x = 72$, what is the value of x?

Question 7

Work out the value of 70^2.

Question 8

What is the sum of 9999 and 999?

Question 9

If the perimeter of an equilateral triangle is 42cm, what is the length of one side?

cm

Question 10

Find the mode(s) of the set of numbers below. Mark your answer(s) below.

5 4 1 5 5 4 3 2 9 1 7 7 7 7 5

3 4 1 9 2 7 5

Question 11

What is the lowest common multiple of 9 and 4?

Question 12

What is the next number in the sequence below?

5 7 12 19 31

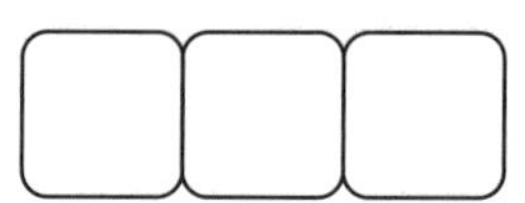

Question 13

What is 30% of 750?

Question 14

In the diagram below, shape A is rotated 180° clockwise about (3,3). What are the new coordinates of point D?

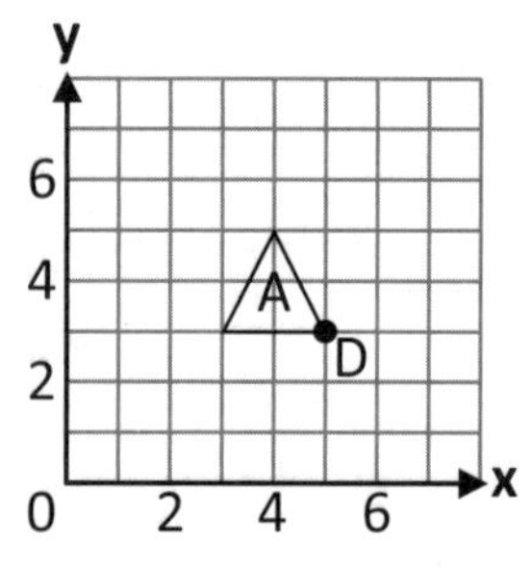

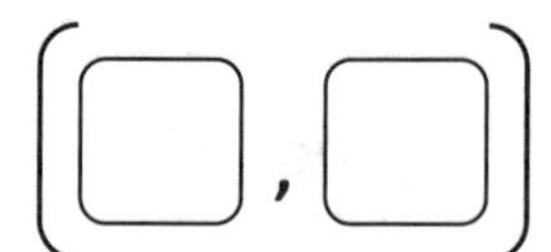

Question 15

What is the highest common factor of 12 and 15?

Question 16

James and Julie's earnings are split in a ratio of 2:5. If Julie earns £65 per day, how much does James earn per day?

£

Question 17

How many squares with sides of length 2cm can fit into a square with sides of length 8cm?

Question 18

Convert 0.032 kilograms into grams.

g

Question 19

Round 5.672 to 2 decimal places.

.

Question 20

In a farm of 80 animals, 24 are sheep. What percentage of animals on the farm are sheep?

%

BLANK PAGE

Short Numerical Reasoning

Test 6

Read the following instructions carefully:

1. You have 6 minutes to complete this test of 20 questions.
2. Work as quickly and carefully as you can.
3. When you have finished a page, go straight onto the next page until you finish the test.
4. You can use all the available space around the question to do your working; however, only write the answer in the answer boxes.
5. To change an answer, rub out your original answer and note down the new answer, aligning it to any answer boxes.
6. If you cannot answer a question, go on to the next question.
7. When you have completed this paper go back to any questions you have missed out and check your answers.
8. Calculators and protractors are not permitted in this test.

Good luck!

After you have finished this paper you can use the 11+ Peer Compare System™ to see how well you performed compared to others who have taken this test. You can register by visiting www.ElevenPlusExams.co.uk/FirstPastThePost to post your results anonymously and obtain the feedback.

Total	**/ 20**

Question 1

What is the missing number in the sequence below?

9	16	25	36	49	

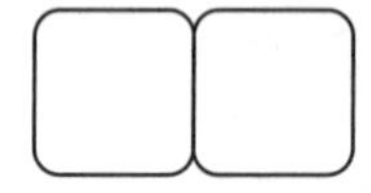

Question 2

Point A is reflected in the y-axis to point B (-1,-6). What were the coordinates of point A?

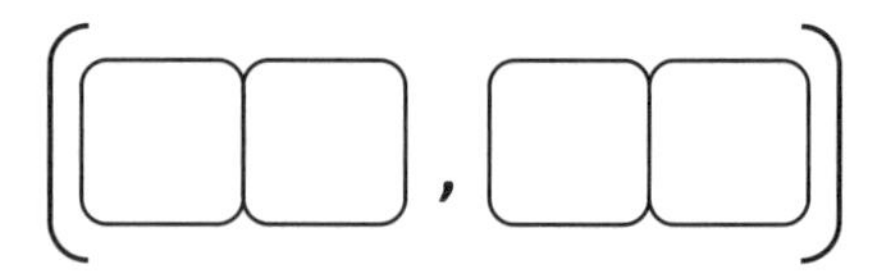

Question 3

The volume of this cuboid is 180cm³. What is the height y?

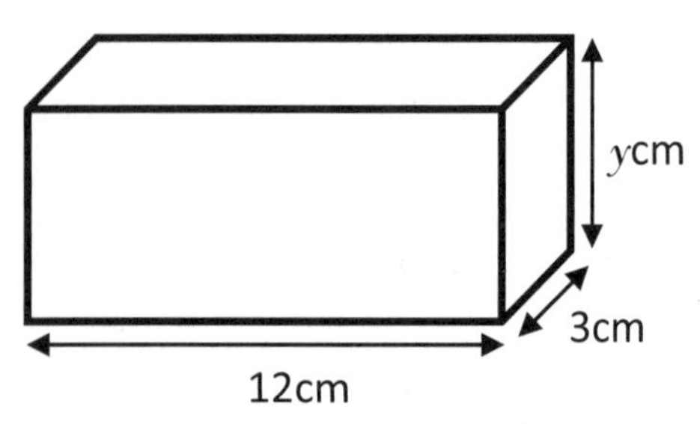

(Diagram not to scale)

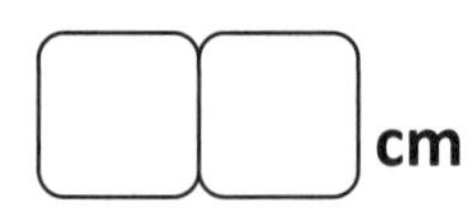

Question 4

What reading is displayed on the weighing scale below?

Question 5

What is the value of 8 × 6 - (45 ÷ 9)?

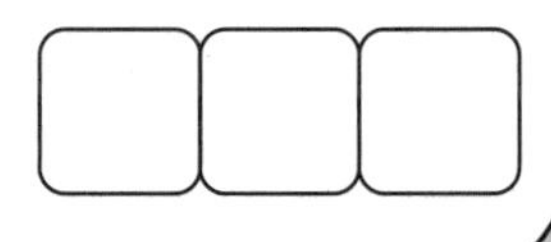

Question 6

What is the next number in the sequence below?

1	8	27	64	

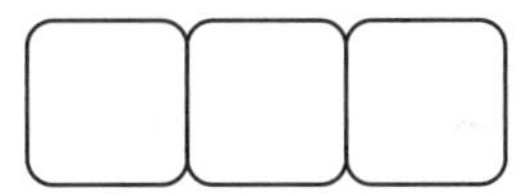

Question 7

Which of the shapes below have a greater volume? Mark your answer below.

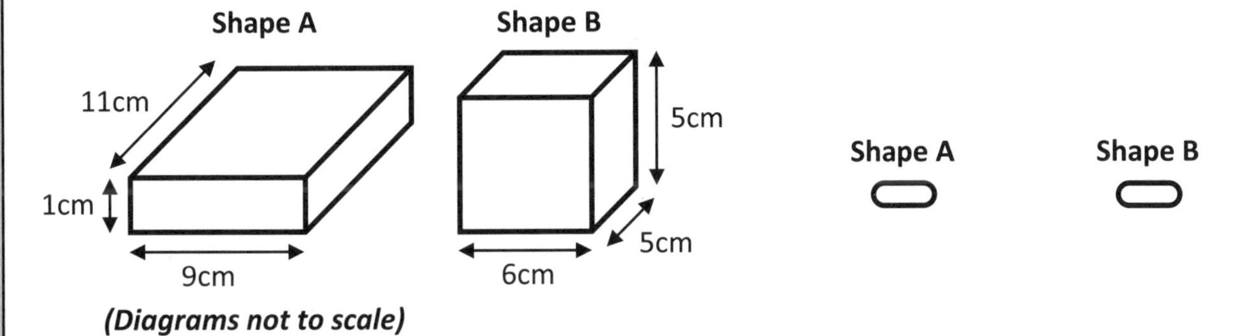

(Diagrams not to scale)

Question 8

Mark all the prime factors of 60 from the numbers given below.

2 3 4 5 6

Question 9

Felix has £1 and £2 coins in the ratio of 1:2 respectively. If he has £50 in total, how many £1 coins does he have?

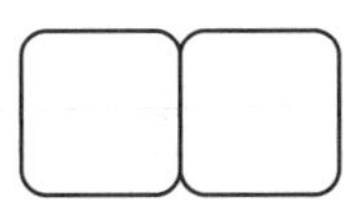

Question 10

What is the value of $\frac{9}{4} + (\frac{1}{4} \times \frac{9}{2})$? Give your answer as a mixed number.

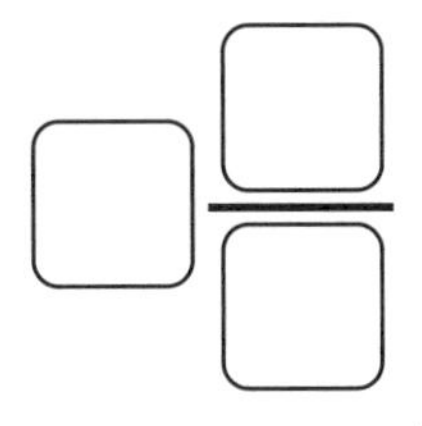

Question 11

How much would a 0.67kg melon and a 183g orange weigh in total?

☐ . ☐☐☐ kg

Question 12

If a triangle has angles of 33°, 47° and 100°, what type of triangle would it be?
Mark your answer below.

Equilateral ⬭ **Isosceles** ⬭ **Scalene** ⬭

Question 13

What is the probability of landing on a number greater than 4 when a fair six-sided die is rolled?

$\frac{\square}{\square}$

Question 14

What is the value of the 8 in 9582370?

☐☐☐☐☐☐☐

Question 15

What is the product of 1^3 and 2^3?

☐☐

Question 16

A survey was conducted to find the most popular holiday destination. How many people in total participated in the survey?

Country	USA	Spain	France	Egypt
Tally	卌 I	卌 卌 III	卌 IIII	卌
Frequency	6	13	9	5

Question 17

What is the sum of the number of lines of symmetry of a square and a rectangle?

Question 18

What is the next number in the sequence below?

3 9 12 36 39

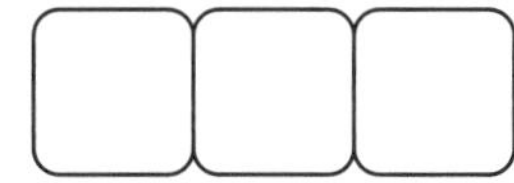

Question 19

How many faces does a square-based pyramid have?

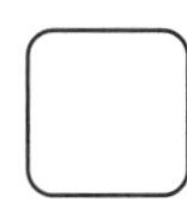

Question 20

Look at the bus timetable below. If James lives in Queensbury, how long would it take him to get to Harrow by bus?

Stops	Times		
Mill Hill	09:20	12:02	14:44
Queensbury	10:00	12:42	15:24
Harrow	10:40	13:22	16:04
Eastcote	11:20	14:02	16:44

minutes

BLANK PAGE

Short Numerical Reasoning

Test 7

Read the following instructions carefully:

1. You have 6 minutes to complete this test of 20 questions.
2. Work as quickly and carefully as you can.
3. When you have finished a page, go straight onto the next page until you finish the test.
4. You can use all the available space around the question to do your working; however, only write the answer in the answer boxes.
5. To change an answer, rub out your original answer and note down the new answer, aligning it to any answer boxes.
6. If you cannot answer a question, go on to the next question.
7. When you have completed this paper go back to any questions you have missed out and check your answers.
8. Calculators and protractors are not permitted in this test.

Good luck!

After you have finished this paper you can use the 11+ Peer Compare System™ to see how well you performed compared to others who have taken this test. You can register by visiting www.ElevenPlusExams.co.uk/FirstPastThePost to post your results anonymously and obtain the feedback.

Total	**/ 20**

Question 1

If $x/_5 = 8$, what is the value of x?

Question 2

If $11x + 3 = 25$, what is the value of x?

Question 3

Emily has 10p and 50p coins in the ratio of 2:7 respectively. If she has eight 10p coins, how much money does she have in total?

£ .

Question 4

What is $^7/_8 \div {}^5/_4$ expressed as a decimal number?

.

Question 5

If a right-angle triangle has an angle of 51°, what is its third angle?

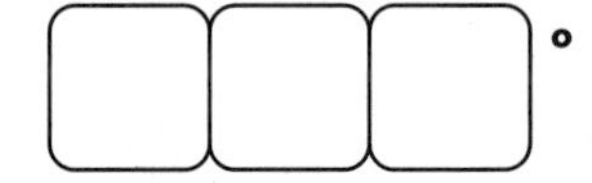

°

Question 6

What is the value of 695 - 272?

Question 7

What is the value of 19 × 3 × 14?

Question 8

What is the missing number in the sequence below?

99	96	90	81	69	

Question 9

What is 4.956 rounded to the nearest whole number?

Question 10

How many sides does an octagon have?

Question 11

If the mean of the set of numbers below is 12, what is the value of x?

11 13 8 15 2 6 x

Question 12

What is the number of lines of symmetry of an isosceles triangle multiplied by the number of lines of symmetry of a square?

Question 13

You are facing West and turn 270° clockwise, which direction are you now facing? Use the compass below to help you.

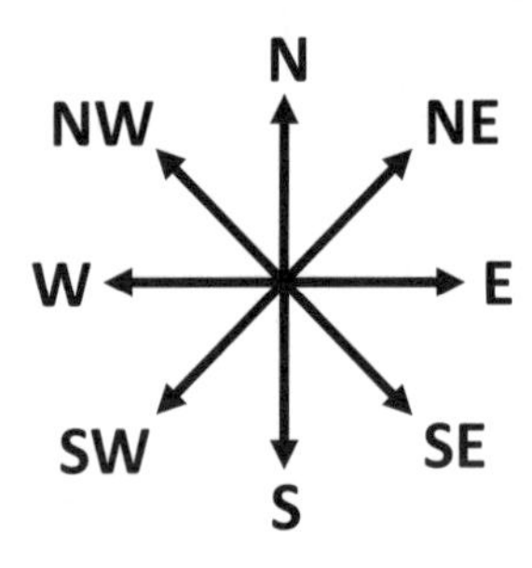

Question 14

What is the value of 4.8 - 2.94?

Question 15

A number machine has an output of 358 and two operations of 'x 41' and '- 11'. What is the input?

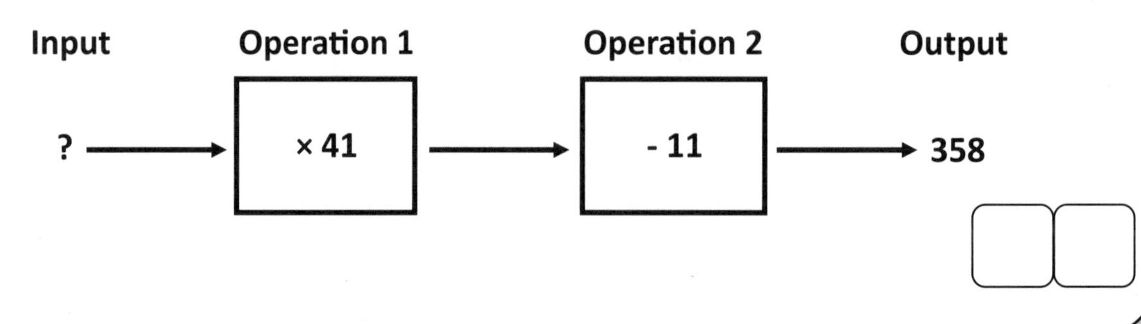

Question 16

Find the median of the set of numbers below.

17 15 14 20 21 27 9 4

Question 17

The mean of set A is 7 and the mean of set B is 24. If there are 4 numbers in each set, what is the combined mean of both Sets A and B?

Question 18

What is 85% of 80?

Question 19

If $7x - 4 = 52$, what is the value of x?

Question 20

What is the value of $12^2 + 5^3$?

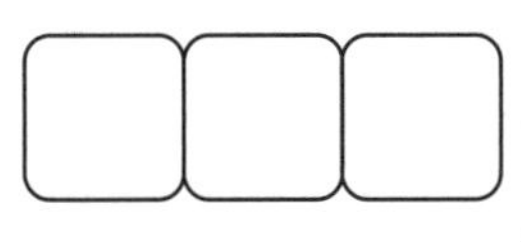

BLANK PAGE

Short Numerical Reasoning

Test 8

Read the following instructions carefully:

1. You have 6 minutes to complete this test of 20 questions.
2. Work as quickly and carefully as you can.
3. When you have finished a page, go straight onto the next page until you finish the test.
4. You can use all the available space around the question to do your working; however, only write the answer in the answer boxes.
5. To change an answer, rub out your original answer and note down the new answer, aligning it to any answer boxes.
6. If you cannot answer a question, go on to the next question.
7. When you have completed this paper go back to any questions you have missed out and check your answers.
8. Calculators and protractors are not permitted in this test.

Good luck!

After you have finished this paper you can use the 11+ Peer Compare System™ to see how well you performed compared to others who have taken this test. You can register by visiting www.ElevenPlusExams.co.uk/FirstPastThePost to post your results anonymously and obtain the feedback.

Total	**/ 20**

Question 1

A number machine has an output of 73 and two operations of '÷ 5' and '+ 68'. What is the input?

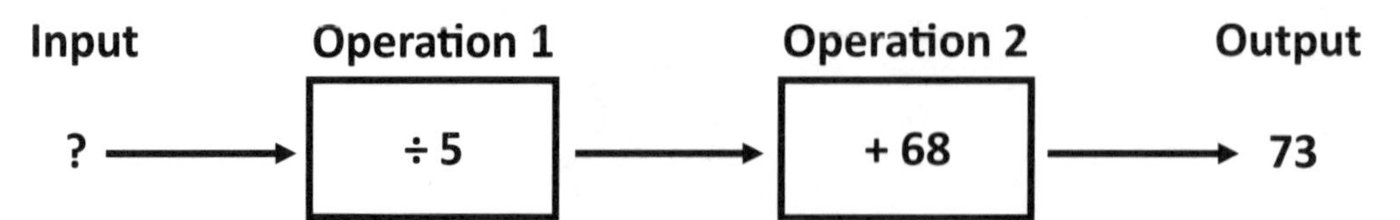

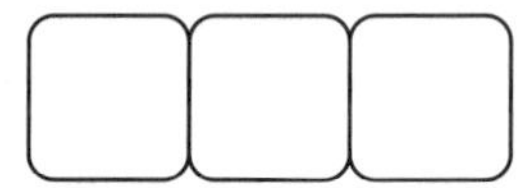

Question 2

How many vertices does a heptagon have?

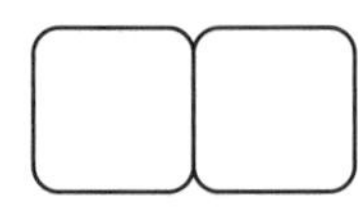

Question 3

John buys 5 cups at £2.99 each. If he pays with a £20 note, how much change will he receive?

Question 4

If $(^x/_{12}) - 10 = 2$, what is the value of x?

Question 5

Convert 8.52 litres into millilitres.

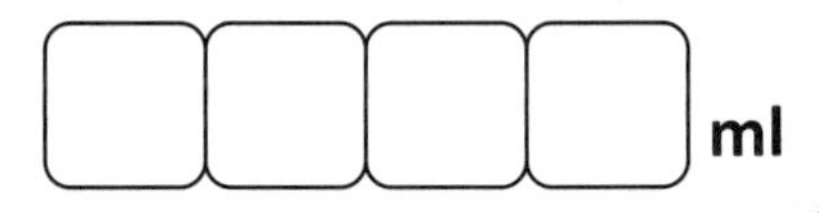

Question 6

A triangle has 3 angles of 60°. What type of triangle is this? Mark your answer below.

Equilateral **Isosceles** **Scalene**

Question 7

Find 3 positive integers that, once squared, add up to 26.

, **and**

Question 8

In a class of 35 students there are 21 girls and the remainder are boys. What is the ratio of boys to girls in the class?

:

Question 9

Find the median of the set of numbers below.

102 111 118 135 97 129 120 80 90

Question 10

If a bottle with a capacity of 500ml is 32% full, how much water is in the bottle?

ml

Question 11

How many pairs of parallel faces does a square-based pyramid have?

Question 12

How many times does 50 go into 1000?

Question 13

45% of children in a football squad support Townsly FC. If 11 children support other teams, how many children are there in the football squad?

Question 14

What is the value of 20.8 ÷ 8?

.

Question 15

Sarah is thinking of a whole cube number. It is greater than 600 but less than 800. What is the number she is thinking of?

Question 16

How many sides does a nonagon have?

Question 17

If $(x \div 4) + 4 = 10$, what is the value of x?

Question 18

In a pet shop, cats and dogs are available in the ratio of 4:5 respectively. If an animal is picked at random, what is the probability of it being a cat?

Question 19

Work out the value of 361 + 567 and then write down the value of the tens.

Question 20

In a bag there are four red balls, three blue balls and three yellow balls. What is the probability of picking a red ball?

BLANK PAGE

Short Numerical Reasoning

Test 9

Read the following instructions carefully:

1. You have 6 minutes to complete this test of 20 questions.
2. Work as quickly and carefully as you can.
3. When you have finished a page, go straight onto the next page until you finish the test.
4. You can use all the available space around the question to do your working; however, only write the answer in the answer boxes.
5. To change an answer, rub out your original answer and note down the new answer, aligning it to any answer boxes.
6. If you cannot answer a question, go on to the next question.
7. When you have completed this paper go back to any questions you have missed out and check your answers.
8. Calculators and protractors are not permitted in this test.

Good luck!

After you have finished this paper you can use the 11+ Peer Compare System™ to see how well you performed compared to others who have taken this test. You can register by visiting www.ElevenPlusExams.co.uk/FirstPastThePost to post your results anonymously and obtain the feedback.

Total	**/ 20**

Question 1

What is the value of $(^3/_4 - {}^1/_4) \div {}^1/_3$? Give your answer as a mixed number.

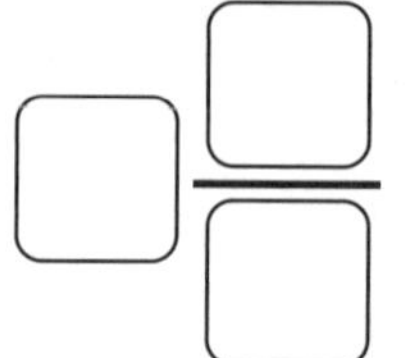

Question 2

What is the next number in the sequence below?

3 6 18 72 360

Question 3

What is the value of $(8 \div 4) + 20 - 3^2$?

Question 4

A set of 9 numbers has a mean of 80. What would be the new mean if the number 70 were added to the set?

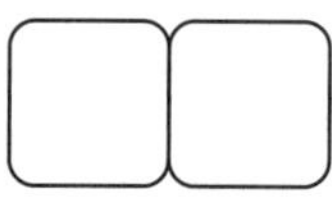

Question 5

What is the lowest common multiple of 3 and 7?

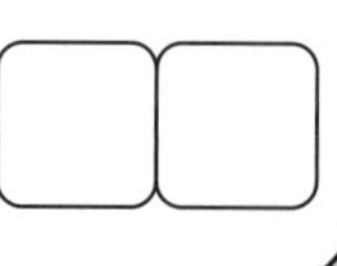

Question 6

What is 150% of 18?

Question 7

How many vertices does a cone have?

Question 8

What is the difference between 50% of 12 and 12% of 50?

Question 9

Convert 1140 millilitres into litres.

. l

Question 10

What is the range of the set of numbers below?

25 **63** **72** **20** **14** **70** **27**

Question 11

How many pairs of parallel faces does a cylinder have?

Question 12

What is the next number in the sequence below?

2 **18** **4** **9** **8** **4.5**

Question 13

What is the product of 9, 16 and 21?

Question 14

In an office there are 4 computers to every 2 laptops. If there are 18 computers, what is the sum of computers and laptops in the office?

Question 15

It is the morning and the time on the clock below is 4 hours and 15 minutes behind the correct time, what is the correct time in 24-hour format?

:

Question 16

What is the difference between the lines of symmetry of a square, and the order of rotational symmetry of a square?

Question 17

Work out 44 + 13 and then give the value of the units.

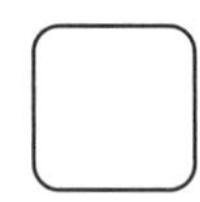

Question 18

The bar graph below displays the favourite movie genres of 150 people. What percentage of people chose romance?

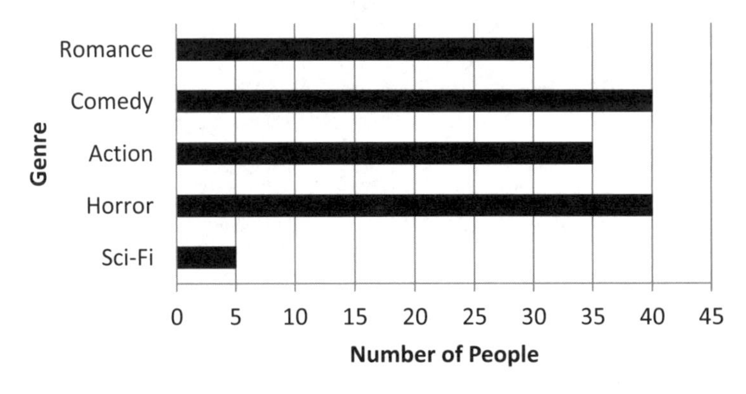

%

Question 19

In a maths test, the highest mark was 90% and the lowest mark was 54%. What is the ratio of the lowest mark to the highest mark in its simplest form?

Question 20

How many vertices does a decagon have?

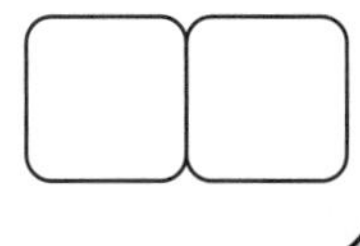

BLANK PAGE

Short Numerical Reasoning

Test 10

Read the following instructions carefully:

1. You have 6 minutes to complete this test of 20 questions.
2. Work as quickly and carefully as you can.
3. When you have finished a page, go straight onto the next page until you finish the test.
4. You can use all the available space around the question to do your working; however, only write the answer in the answer boxes.
5. To change an answer, rub out your original answer and note down the new answer, aligning it to any answer boxes.
6. If you cannot answer a question, go on to the next question.
7. When you have completed this paper go back to any questions you have missed out and check your answers.
8. Calculators and protractors are not permitted in this test.

Good luck!

After you have finished this paper you can use the 11+ Peer Compare System™ to see how well you performed compared to others who have taken this test. You can register by visiting www.ElevenPlusExams.co.uk/FirstPastThePost to post your results anonymously and obtain the feedback.

Total	**/ 20**

Question 1

What is the value of $20 \div 5 + 5^2 - (2 \times 11)$?

Question 2

If $(13x + 1) - 5 = 35$, what is the value of x?

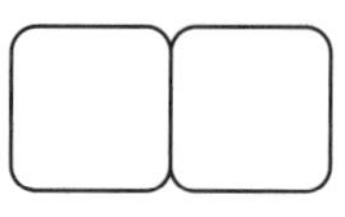

Question 3

A point with coordinates (3,-4) is reflected in the y-axis and then in the x-axis. What are the new coordinates of this point?

Question 4

What is the perimeter of the rectangle shown below?

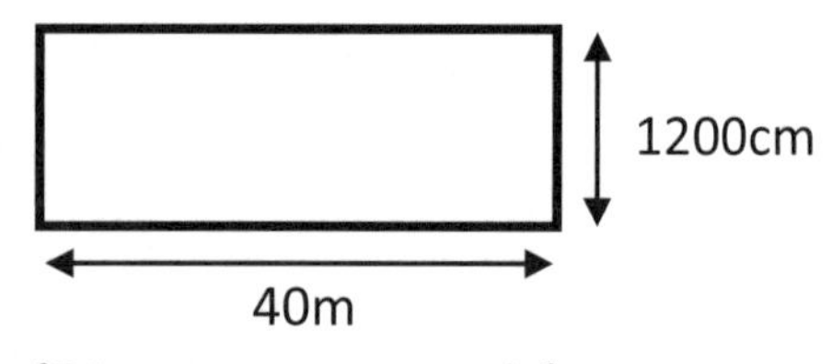

(Diagram not to scale)

Question 5

If wooden chairs cost £14.98 each, how much will 5 wooden chairs cost?

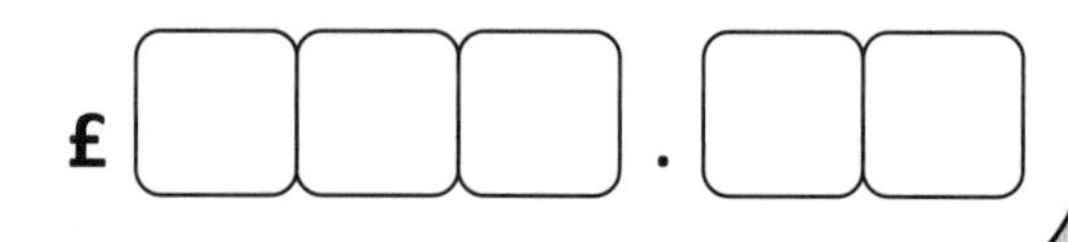

Question 6

What is $^{16}/_{3}$ - $^{5}/_{6}$? Give your answer as a simplified improper fraction.

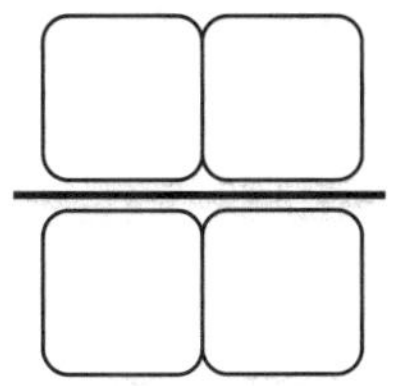

Question 7

If Jamie runs 10.5km every hour, how far will he run in 1.5 hours?

Question 8

Whilst tossing a fair coin, what is the probability of it landing on heads twice in a row?

Question 9

What is the value of 6073 - 5069?

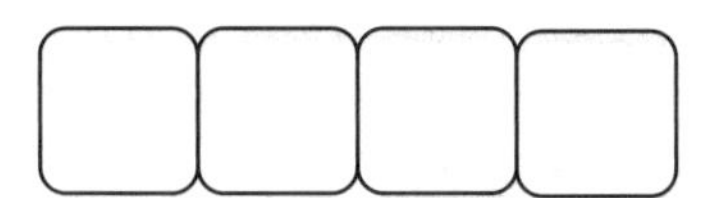

Question 10

200 pupils at a local secondary school were surveyed to find out which country they are supporting at the football World Cup. 20 pupils are supporting country 2. Work out the angle represented by country 2.

Number of Pupils Supporting Each Country

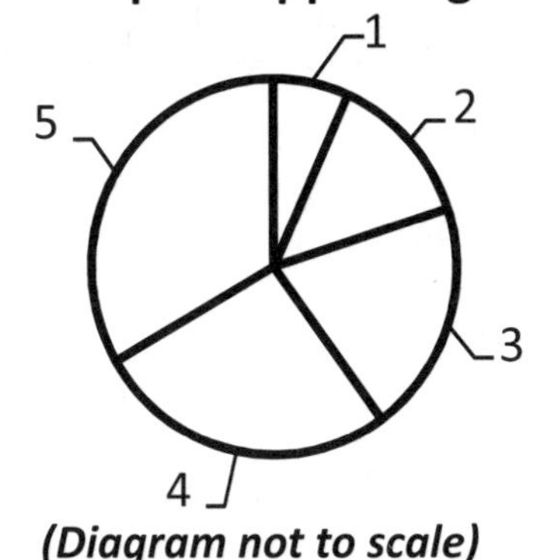

(Diagram not to scale)

°

Question 11

During the day, Tina consumed 1987 calories and Mike consumed 2439 calories. What is the difference between the number of calories consumed by Tina and Mike?

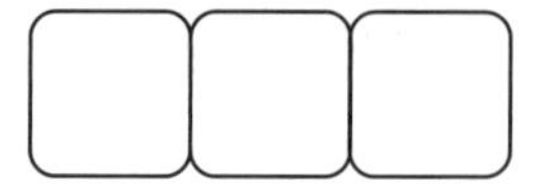

Question 12

A triangle has two angles of 75° and a third angle of 30°. What type of triangle is this? Mark your answer below.

Equilateral **Isosceles** **Scalene**

Question 13

If 99% of x is 99, what is the value of x?

Question 14

If the time now is 2.12pm, what was the time 6 hours and 30 minutes ago?

Question 15

What is 2520ml + 0.78l?

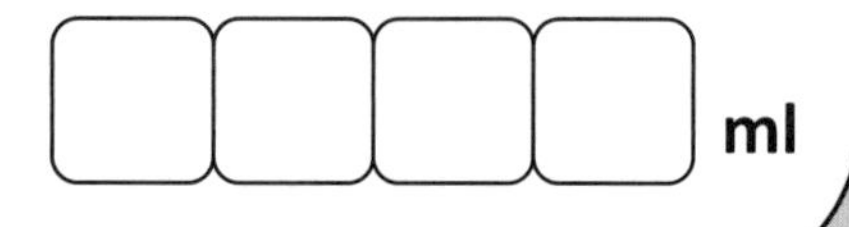

Question 16

A box contains black and white marbles. If there are 99 marbles in the box and $^7/_9$ of them are black, how many white marbles are there?

Question 17

How many lines of symmetry does a rhombus have?

Question 18

What is the probability of picking a club at random from a complete deck of 52 cards?

Question 19

What is the highest common factor of 26 and 42?

Question 20

What is the order of rotational symmetry of an equilateral triangle?

BLANK PAGE

FIRST PAST THE POST® SERIES

Short Numerical Reasoning

Book 1

Answers and Explanations

As you complete each question, remember that you can use the 11+ Peer Compare System™ to see how well you performed in comparison to others who have taken this test.

You can register by visiting www.ElevenPlusExams.co.uk/FirstPastThePost to post your results anonymously and obtain the feedback.

Your unique 16 digit access code is:

IYWX-10IA-J6PK-V19I

Test 1

Question	Answer	Explanation
1	**13**	Input × 5 = 65. Therefore, input = 65 ÷ 5 = 13.
2	**7**	Subtract 14 from both sides of the equation to make x the subject: 21 - 14 = 7. Therefore x = 7.
3	**10**	The mean is found by adding all the numbers in the set together and dividing by the number of values in the set. (7 + 5 + 17 + 12 + 15 + 4) ÷ 6 = 60 ÷ 6 = 10.
4	**$7\,{}^{4}/_{9}$**	First find out how many times 9 can fully go into 67, which is 7. Because 9 × 7 = 63, this leaves a remainder of 4, and so the answer is 7 and ${}^{4}/_{9}$.
5	**252cm^3**	Volume = length × width × height. Volume = 9cm × 7cm × 4cm = 252cm^3.
6	**256cm^2**	Area of square = 16cm × 16cm = 256cm^2.
7	**7:9**	The ratio of boys to girls is 14:18. This can be simplified to 7:9 by dividing through by 2.
8	**W**	Each increment is equivalent to 45°, 135° ÷ 45° = 3. Therefore you must turn 3 increments anticlockwise from NE to get to W.
9	**9**	Using BIDMAS, first work out the sum in the brackets (12 - 5 = 7). Then work out 2^2 = 4. This gives 7 + 1 - 4 + 5 = 9.
10	**5**	A pentagon has 5 sides.
11	**15:45**	As the time given, 3.45pm, is followed by 'pm' you must add on 12 hours to give the 24-hour equivalent, giving 15:45.
12	**3000**	3 is in the thousands column and therefore it represents 3000.
13	**18cm^2**	Area of rectangle = base × height = 6cm × 5cm = 30cm^2. Area of triangle = ${}^{1}/_{2}$ × base × height = ${}^{1}/_{2}$ × 8cm × 12cm = 48cm^2. Difference = 48cm^2 - 30cm^2 = 18cm^2.
14	**13.25m**	100cm = 1m. Divide 1325cm by 100 to get 13.25m.
15	**275cm^3**	Multiply the surface area of the pentagonal face by the length of the prism; 25cm^2 × 11cm = 275cm^3.
16	**(0,10)**	For the x-coordinate, -5 + 5 = 0. For the y-coordinate, 8 + 2 = 10.
17	**350ml**	Each division is 50ml. The water in the bottle is one division above 300ml. Therefore, 300ml + 50ml = 350ml.
18	**2**	Rotational symmetry is when a shape is rotated but still seems to have the same original position. A rectangle has a rotational symmetry of order 2. This is because when a rectangle is rotated through 360°, it takes the shape of its original position 2 times.
19	**9**	An edge is the line joining two adjacent vertices. There are 9 edges in a triangular prism.
20	**180**	15% of children chose swimming as their favourite sport. 15% of 1200 = 0.15 × 1200 = 180.

Test 2

Question	Answer	Explanation
1	**30m**	The perimeter is the total distance around the outside of a shape. Perimeter = 12m + 3m + 12m + 3m = 30m.
2	**8**	This shape has two hexagonal faces and a further 6 faces corresponding to each side of the hexagon, therefore in total there are 8 faces.
3	**80cm^3**	Multiply the surface area of the triangular face by the length of the prism. Area of face = 5cm × 4cm × $^1/_2$ = 10cm^2. Volume = 10cm^2 × 8cm = 80cm^3.
4	**3**	Opposite faces are parallel; therefore there are 3 pairs (6 faces in total).
5	**72**	Input - 59 = 13. Therefore, input = 13 + 59 = 72.
6	**Obtuse**	Angles between 90° and 180° are called obtuse angles.
7	**$^1/_{13}$**	Out of the 52 cards, 4 of them are aces. Therefore there is a $^4/_{52}$ chance of picking an ace at random. This can be simplified to $^1/_{13}$ by dividing through by 4.
8	**70**	7 is in the tens column and therefore it represents 70.
9	**43**	387 ÷ 9 = 43.
10	**(7,5)**	The fourth coordinate must be vertically above (7,2) and horizontally in line with (2,5) in order to complete the rectangle. Therefore its coordinates are (7,5).
11	**Equilateral**	Equilateral triangles have 3 lines of symmetry. Scalene triangles have no lines of symmetry. Isosceles triangles have one line of symmetry.
12	**13:00**	210 minutes is 3 hours and 30 minutes. 3 hours and 30 minutes after 09:30 is 13:00.
13	**4**	A vertex is a point at which two or more edges meet. A kite has four vertices.
14	**6cm**	Volume = length × area of cross sectional face. Length = volume ÷ area of cross sectional face. 192cm^3 ÷ 32cm^2 = 6cm.
15	**3**	A prime number is any number above 1 which can only be divided by 1 and itself. 31, 2 and 41 are all prime numbers.
16	**$^{43}/_{10}$**	Multiply 4 by 10 to get 40, and then add 3 to get 43. The answer will be $^{43}/_{10}$.
17	**6**	In this sequence you add 7 to find the next term. By reversing the operation we can find the missing term, hence 13 - 7 = 6 .
18	**48m**	The perimeter is the total distance around the outside of a shape. Perimeter = 12m × 4 = 12m + 12m + 12m + 12m = 48m.
19	**86**	The difference between each term increases by 2 every time, i.e. the sequence progresses through a pattern of '+2, +4, +6, +8'. Therefore, the next difference will be 10; 76 + 10 = 86.
20	**68%**	A percentage is a fraction of 100; $^{34}/_{50}$ = $^{68}/_{100}$ = 68%. Alternatively, 34 ÷ 50 = 0.68; 0.68 × 100 = 68%.

Test 3

Question	Answer	Explanation
1	**1920**	8 × 12 × 20 = 1920.
2	**Thursday**	There are 14 days between 5th September and 19th September. This is equal to 2 weeks so 19th September will also fall on a Thursday.
3	**52**	$5^2 = 25$; $3^3 = 27$; 25 + 27 = 52.
4	**94**	282 ÷ 3 = 94.
5	**12.55pm**	Daniel takes 35 minutes to get to Harrow because he takes 15 less than Ashley. 35 minutes before 1.30pm is 12.55pm.
6	**18 units^2**	Area = height × base × $^1/_2$. The base is given by the difference between the coordinates (4,1) and (4,7) which is 6 units. The height is given by the difference between the coordinates (4,1) and (10,1), which is also 6. Therefore, area = 6 units × 6 units × $^1/_2$ = 18 units^2.
7	**3:6:2**	The ratio of zebras to monkeys to elephants is 6:12:4. This can be simplified to 3:6:2 by dividing through by 2.
8	**52000cm**	1km = 100000cm. Multiply 0.52km by 100000 to get 52000cm.
9	**128**	Input ÷ 8 = 16. Therefore, input = 16 × 8 = 128.
10	**6**	An edge is the line joining two adjacent vertices. There are 6 edges in a triangular based pyramid.
11	**75mm^2**	Area = $^1/_2$ × base x height = $^1/_2$ × 15mm × 10mm = 75mm^2.
12	**58°**	Angles in a triangle add up to 180°; 96° + 26°= 122°. Therefore 180° - 122° = 58°.
13	**£81.50**	£28 + £19 + £34.50 = £81.50.
14	**160**	25 + 20 + 60 + 10 + 45 = 160.
15	**24**	The smallest number that appears in both the 8 times table and the 12 times table is 24.
16	**1.7°C**	-0.8°C + 2.5°C = 1.7°C.
17	**5 and 6**	Identify the section of the graph which is a horizontal straight line, i.e. there is no increase or decrease in the number of train delays from one day to the next.
18	**Isosceles**	The third angle in this triangle must be 45° as 180° - 90° - 45° = 45° and angles in a triangle add up to 180°. Therefore there are two equal angles so this triangle is an isosceles triangle.
19	**41**	Add 9 to both sides of the equation. 32 + 9 = 41. Therefore x = 41.
20	**(3,6)**	Using the x-axis as a mirror line, only the y-coordinate of the point P will be changed, becoming (3,6).

Test 4

Question	Answer	Explanation
1	**(4,-1)**	For the x-coordinate, 8 - 4 = 4. For the y-coordinate, -4 + 3 = -1.
2	**83**	Using BIDMAS, first work out the sum in the brackets $(2^3 - 1) = (8 - 1) = 7$. This gives 54 + 36 - 7 = 90 - 7 = 83.
3	**15**	The sequence of triangular numbers is: 1, 3, 6, 10, 15, … . 15 is the next triangular number after 10.
4	**4**	Rotational symmetry is when a shape is rotated but still seems to have the same original position. A square has a rotational symmetry of order 4. This is because when a square is rotated through 360°, it takes the shape of its original position 4 times.
5	**27**	Work out the volume of the two cubes: $3^3 = 27$ and $1^3 = 1$ respectively. 27 ÷ 1 = 27 times.
6	**5m**	Perimeter of triangle = 5m + 8m + 12m = 25m. Perimeter of parallelogram = 7m + 8m + 7m + 8m = 30m. Difference = 30m - 25m = 5m.
7	**201**	Input - 47 = 154. Therefore, input 154 + 47 = 201.
8	**8**	A vertex is the point at which two or more edges meet. A cube has 8 vertices.
9	**27**	Range = largest value - smallest value = 34 - 7 = 27.
10	**49**	$6^2 = 6 \times 6 = 36$ which is less than 40; $8^2 = 8 \times 8 = 64$ which is greater than 50. Therefore, the answer is 49 as $7^2 = 7 \times 7$.
11	**Parallel**	The lines are parallel as even if they are extended, they will never cross.
12	**31-45**	The modal group is the group which has the highest frequency (largest tally). In this case, the group 31-45 has a frequency of 11.
13	**72**	The first three multiples of 6 greater than 15 are 18, 24 and 30; 18 + 24 + 30 = 72.
14	**(3,3)**	Rotating the x-coordinate 90° anticlockwise about the origin gives 3. Rotating the y-coordinate 90° anticlockwise about the origin gives 3.
15	**8.01m**	1000mm = 1m. Divide 8010mm by 1000 to get 8.01m.
16	**120cm^2**	Area = base × height = 12cm × 10cm = 120cm^2.
17	**135°**	Each increment on the compass is 45°. Mary is walking SE which is 3 increments from N. 3 × 45° = 135°. Therefore, this gives a bearing of 135°.
18	**721**	457 + 264 = 721.
19	**157cm**	Each division on the scale is equal to 1cm. His initial height, marked on the ruler, is therefore 152cm; 152cm + 5cm = 157cm.
20	**9:2**	The ratio of pencils to pens is 54:12. This can be simplified to 9:2 by dividing through by 6.

Test 5

Question	Answer	Explanation
1	**0.114km**	1km = 1000m. Change all units to m, giving 70m + 18m + 26m = 114m; 114m = 0.114km.
2	**12**	An edge is the line joining two adjacent vertices. There are 12 edges in a cube.
3	**4.73kg**	1000g = 1kg. Divide 4730g by 1000 to get 4.73kg.
4	**4**	A regular pentagon has 5 lines of symmetry. An isosceles triangle has 1; 5 - 1 = 4.
5	**10cm**	Volume = length × area of triangle. Length = volume ÷ area of triangle. Length = 60cm^3 ÷ 6cm^2 = 10cm.
6	**12**	Divide both sides of the equation by 6; 72 ÷ 6 = 12. Therefore x = 12.
7	**4900**	70^2 = 70 × 70 = 4900.
8	**10998**	9999 + 999 = 10998.
9	**14cm**	The sides of an equilateral triangle are of equal length. Therefore, the length of one side is 42cm ÷ 3 = 14cm.
10	**5 and 7**	The mode is the most common value in a set of data. In this set of data there are two modal values as there are four 5s and four 7s.
11	**36**	The smallest number that appears in both the 9 times table and the 4 times table is 36.
12	**50**	The next term in this sequence is found by adding together the previous two terms. Hence, to find the next term you must find the sum of the last two terms: 19 + 31 = 50.
13	**225**	10% of 750 is 75; 30% = 75 × 3 = 225. Alternatively, 750 × 0.3 = 225.
14	**(1,3)**	When the triangle is rotated 180° about (3,3), point D will have coordinates of (1,3).
15	**3**	The biggest number that divides into both 12 and 15 is 3; 3 × 4 = 12 and 3 × 5 = 15.
16	**£26**	As Julie earns £65, we know that 5 units = £65; £65 ÷ 5 = £13, therefore 1 unit = £13. James earns 2 units which is £13 x 2 = £26.
17	**16**	The area of the square with 2cm sides is 4cm^2. The area of the square with 8cm sides is 64 cm^2. The smaller square fits into the larger square 16 times as 64 ÷ 4 = 16.
18	**32g**	1000g = 1kg. Multiply 0.032kg by 1000 to get 32g.
19	**5.67**	The digit in the third decimal place is 2. This is less than 5, so it is rounded down. 5.672 rounded to 2 decimal places is 5.67.
20	**30%**	A percentage is a fraction of 100; $^{24}/_{80}$ = $^{30}/_{100}$ = 30%. Alternatively, 24 ÷ 80 = 0.3; 0.3 × 100 = 30%.

Test 6

Question	Answer	Explanation
1	**64**	This is a sequence of square numbers. The last term given is $7^2 = 49$. Therefore the next term is 64 as $8^2 = 8 \times 8 = 64$.
2	**(1,-6)**	In order to work out the coordinates of point A, the transformation must be reversed. This point is reflected in the y-axis, so only the x-coordinate is changed, becoming (1,-6).
3	**5cm**	Volume = length × width × height = 12cm × 3cm × y = 180cm^2; y = 180cm^2 ÷ 36cm = 5cm.
4	**0.5kg**	Each division is 100g. Therefore the reading on the scale is 500g which is equivalent to 0.5kg.
5	**43**	Using BIDMAS, first work out the sum in the brackets (45 ÷ 9) = 5. Then work out the multiplication 8 × 6 = 48. This gives 48 - 5 = 43.
6	**125**	This is a sequence of cube numbers. The last term given is $4^3 = 4 \times 4 \times 4 = 64$. Therefore the next term is 125 as $5^3 = 5 \times 5 \times 5 = 125$.
7	**Shape B**	Volume = length × width × height. Volume of shape A = 11cm × 9cm × 1cm = 99cm^3. Volume of shape B = 6cm × 5cm × 5cm = 150cm^3.
8	**2, 3, 5**	Of the numbers given, 2, 3 and 5 are the only ones that can be divided into 60 and are prime numbers.
9	**10**	(£1 × 10) + (£2 × 20) = £50. Therefore there are ten £1 coins and twenty £2 coins.
10	**$3\ {}^{3}/_{8}$**	Using BIDMAS, first work out the product of the fractions in the brackets by multiplying the numerators and denominators, to get ${}^{9}/_{8}$. Then complete the addition, ${}^{9}/_{4} + {}^{9}/_{8} = {}^{18}/_{8} + {}^{9}/_{8} = {}^{27}/_{8}$. To convert ${}^{27}/_{8}$ a mixed number divide through by 8. This gives 3 and a remainder of 3, giving $3\ {}^{3}/_{8}$.
11	**0.853kg**	1000g = 1kg. Change all units to kg, giving 0.67kg + 0.183kg = 0.853kg.
12	**Scalene**	All three angles in the triangle are different, so this is a scalene triangle.
13	**${}^{1}/_{3}$**	There are only two numbers greater than 4 on a fair six-sided die, 5 and 6. Therefore the probability of landing on one of these when a fair die is rolled is ${}^{2}/_{6}$. This can be simplified to ${}^{1}/_{3}$ by dividing through by 2.
14	**80000**	8 is in the ten thousands column and therefore it represents 80000.
15	**8**	$1^3 = 1$; $2^3 = 8$; $1 \times 8 = 8$.
16	**33**	6 + 13 + 9 + 5 = 33.
17	**6**	A square has 4 lines of symmetry. A rectangle has 2 lines of symmetry. 4 + 2 = 6.
18	**117**	This sequence progresses according to the pattern '× 3, + 3, × 3, + 3'. Therefore, to work out the next number you must calculate 39 × 3 which is 117.
19	**5**	This shape has a square base and a further 4 faces corresponding to each side of the square, therefore in total there are 5 faces.
20	**40 minutes**	One bus leaves Queensbury at 10:00 and reaches Harrow at 10:40. Therefore, it should take James 40 minutes to get to Harrow.

Test 7

Question	Answer	Explanation
1	**40**	Multiply both sides of the equation by 5; 8 × 5 = 40. Therefore x = 40.
2	**2**	Firstly, subtract 3 from both sides to get 11x = 22. Then divide both sides by 11; 22 ÷ 11 = 2. Therefore x = 2.
3	**£14.80**	As Emily has eight 10p coins, we know that 2 units = 8. Therefore, 1 unit = 4. As the ratio of 10p coins to 50p coins is 2:7, she must have twenty eight 50p coins as 4 × 7 = 28. (8 x £0.10) + (28 x £0.50) = £14.80.
4	**0.7**	$^7/_8 \div {^5/_4} = {^7/_8} \times {^4/_5} = {^{28}/_{40}}$. This can be simplified to $^7/_{10}$ by dividing through by 4. This is 0.7 as a decimal.
5	**39°**	Angles in a triangle add up to 180°. One of the angles must be 90°; 90° + 51° = 141°; 180° - 141° = 39°.
6	**423**	695 - 272 = 423.
7	**798**	19 × 3 × 14 = 798.
8	**54**	The number subtracted between each term increases by 3 every time, i.e. the sequence progresses through a pattern of '- 3, - 6, - 9, -12'. Therefore the next term is given by 69 - 15 = 54.
9	**5**	The digit in the first decimal place is 9. This is greater than 5, so it is rounded up. Therefore 4.956 rounded to the nearest whole number is 5.
10	**8**	An octagon has 8 sides.
11	**29**	The mean is found by adding all the numbers in the set together and dividing by the number of values in the set. 12 = (11 + 13 + 8 + 15 + 2 + 6 + x) ÷ 7; 12 = (55 + x) ÷ 7; 12 × 7 = 84 = 55 + x. Therefore x = 29.
12	**4**	An isosceles triangle has 1 line of symmetry. A square has 4 lines of symmetry. 1 × 4 = 4.
13	**S**	Each increment is equivalent to 45°. As 270° ÷ 45° = 6, this means you must turn through 6 increments clockwise from W to get to S.
14	**1.86**	4.8 - 2.94 = 1.86.
15	**9**	Input × 41 - 11 = 358. First, add 11 to both sides of the equation; input × 41 = 369. Therefore, input = 369 ÷ 41 = 9.
16	**16**	The median is the middle value when all values in a set of data are ordered in terms of size: 4, 9, 14, 15, 17, 20, 21 and 27. There are 8 numbers in this data set, so the median is the mean of the fourth and fifth number. Median = (15 + 17) ÷ 2 = 16.
17	**15.5**	The mean is found by adding all the numbers in the set together and dividing by the number of values in the set. First find the sum of all the numbers in each set: 7 × 4 = 28; 24 × 4 = 96. Therefore, mean = (96 + 28) ÷ 8 = 124 ÷ 8 = 15.5.
18	**68**	10% of 80 is 80 × 0.1 = 8; 85% = 8 × 8.5 = 68. Alternatively, 0.85 × 80 = 68.
19	**8**	Firstly, add 4 to both sides of the equation to get 7x = 56. Then divide both sides by 7; 56 ÷ 7 = 8. Therefore x=8.
20	**269**	12^2 = 144; 5^3 = 125; 144 + 125 = 269.

Test 8

Question	Answer	Explanation
1	**25**	Input ÷ 5 + 68 = 73. First subtract 68 from both sides of the equation; 73 - 68 = 5. Then
2	**7**	A vertex is the point at which two or more edges meet. A heptagon has seven vertices.
3	**£5.05**	£20.00 - 5 × £2.99 = £20.00 - £14.95 = £5.05.
4	**144**	Add 10 to both sides of the equation to get $x/_{12}$ = 12. Then multiply both sides by 12; 12 x 12 = 144. Therefore x = 144.
5	**8520ml**	1l = 1000ml. Multiply 8.52l by 1000 to get 8520ml.
6	**Equilateral**	All three angles are equal, so this is an equilateral triangle.
7	**1, 3 and 4**	$1^2 + 3^2 + 4^2 = 1 + 9 + 16 = 26$.
8	**2:3**	The number of boys is 35 - 21 = 14. The ratio of boys to girls is 14:21. This can be simplified to 2:3 by dividing through by 7.
9	**111**	The median is the middle value when all values in a set of data are ordered in terms of size: 80, 90, 97, 102, 111, 118, 120, 129 and 135. There are 9 numbers in this data set, so the median is the fifth largest or fifth smallest, which in this case is 111.
10	**160ml**	500ml × 0.32 = 160ml.
11	**0**	Each face is at an angle to the adjacent faces, and so none are parallel.
12	**20**	1000 ÷ 50 = 20.
13	**20**	100% - 45% = 55%. 55% = 11, therefore 1% = 11 ÷ 55, and 100% = (11 ÷ 55) × 100 = 20.
14	**2.6**	20.8 ÷ 8 = 2.6.
15	**729**	$10^3 = 10 \times 10 \times 10 = 1000$. Therefore begin by working backwards from 10; $9^3 = 9 \times 9 \times 9 = 729$. This lies between 600 and 800.
16	**9**	A nonagon has 9 sides .
17	**24**	Subtract 4 from both sides to get $x \div 4 = 6$. Then multiply both sides by 4; $x = 6 \times 4$. Therefore $x = 24$.
18	**$^4/_9$**	For every 4 cats, there are 5 dogs, so $^4/_9$ animals are cats.
19	**20**	361 + 567 = 928. The number 2 is in the tens column and therefore it represents 20.
20	**$^2/_5$**	Work out the total number of balls in the bag: 4 + 3 + 3 = 10. The probability of picking a red ball is $^4/_{10}$. This can be simplified to $^2/_5$ by dividing through by 2.

Test 9

Question	Answer	Explanation
1	**$1\frac{1}{2}$**	Firstly subtract the fractions inside the brackets. $\frac{3}{4} - \frac{1}{4} = \frac{2}{4}$. This can be simplified to $\frac{1}{2}$ by dividing through by 2. Then complete the rest of the sum: $\frac{1}{2} \div \frac{1}{3} = \frac{1}{2} \times \frac{3}{1} = \frac{3}{2}$. This is $1\frac{1}{2}$ as a mixed number.
2	**2160**	The terms are multiplied in the sequence according to the pattern '× 2, × 3, × 4, × 5'. Therefore the next term is 360 × 6 = 2160.
3	**13**	Using BIDMAS, first work out the sum in the brackets (8 ÷ 4 = 2) and then the indices; $3^2 = 9$. This gives 2 + 20 - 9 = 13.
4	**79**	The mean is found by adding all the numbers in the set together and dividing by the number of values in the set. 80 × 9 = 720 gives the original total. 720 + 70 = 790 gives the new total. The new mean is therefore 790 ÷ 10 = 79.
5	**21**	The smallest number that appears in both the 3 times table and the 7 times table is 21.
6	**27**	50% of 18 is 18 × 0.5 = 9; 50% × 3 = 150% = 9 × 3 = 27. Alternatively, 18 × 1.5 = 27.
7	**1**	A vertex is the point at which two or more edges meet. A cone has a circular base and so only has one corner at the top.
8	**0**	50% of 12 is 12 × 0.5 = 6; 12% of 50 is 50 × 0.12 = 6. Both sums have the same value so the difference between them is 0.
9	**1.14l**	1l = 1000ml. Divide 1140ml by 1000 to get 1.14l.
10	**58**	Range = largest value - smallest value = 72 - 14 = 58.
11	**1**	A cylinder has two circular faces that are opposite each other, therefore they are parallel and so there is one pair of parallel faces.
12	**16**	There are two patterns within one sequence here, the first starts with 2, and the second with 18. To find the next term in the first pattern '× 2' but in the second one '÷ 2'. The next term in the series is 16, as 8 × 2 = 16.
13	**3024**	9 × 16 × 21 = 3024.
14	**27**	The ratio of computers to laptops is 4:2. This can be simplified to 2:1 by dividing through by 2. If there are 18 computers, there are half as many laptops, 9. Therefore the total is 18 + 9 = 27.
15	**07:45**	The time on the clock reads 03:30am. As the clock is 4 hours and 15 minutes behind, the actual time is 07:45am.
16	**0**	A square has 4 lines of symmetry. The order of rotational symmetry of a square is 4; 4 - 4 = 0.
17	**7**	44 + 13 = 57. The number 7 is in the units column.
18	**20%**	A percentage is a fraction of 100; $\frac{30}{150} = \frac{20}{100}$ = 20%. Alternatively, 30 ÷ 150 = 0.2; 0.2 × 100 = 20%.
19	**3:5**	The ratio of the lowest mark to the highest mark is 54:90. This can be simplified to 3:5 by dividing through by 18.
20	**10**	A decagon has 10 sides.

Test 10

Question	Answer	Explanation
1	**7**	Using BIDMAS, first work out the sum in the brackets (2 × 11 = 22). Then work out the indices 5^2 = 25 and then 20 ÷ 5 = 4. This gives 4 + 25 - 22 = 7.
2	**3**	Firstly, add 5 to both sides of the equation to get $13x + 1 = 40$. Then subtract 1 from both sides to get $13x = 39$. Lastly, divide both sides by 13; 39 ÷ 13 = 3. Therefore x= 3.
3	**(-3,4)**	When (3,-4) is reflected in the y-axis, it becomes (-3,-4). When (-3,-4) is reflected in the x-axis, it becomes (-3,4).
4	**104m**	First convert all lengths into the same units, 1200cm = 12m. The perimeter is the total distance around the outside of a shape. Perimeter = 12m + 40m + 12m + 40m = 104m.
5	**£74.90**	5 × £14.98 = £74.90.
6	$^{9}/_{2}$	Firstly find a common denominator, in this case it is 6, and adjust the fractions to give you $^{32}/_{6} - ^{5}/_{6} = ^{27}/_{6}$. This can be simplified to $^{9}/_{2}$ by dividing through by 3.
7	**15.75km**	10.5 km per hour × 1.5 hours = 15.75km.
8	$^{1}/_{4}$	There are two possible outcomes of tossing a fair coin, one of which is heads. Therefore, the probability of landing on heads is $^{1}/_{2}$. The probability of this occurring twice in a row is $^{1}/_{2} \times ^{1}/_{2} = ^{1}/_{4}$.
9	**1004**	6073 - 5069 = 1004.
10	**36°**	The angle about a point is 360°. $^{20}/_{200}$ × 360° = 36°.
11	**452**	2439 - 1987 = 452.
12	**Isosceles**	Two angles in the triangle are the same, so this is an isosceles triangle.
13	**100**	As 99% = 99, 1% = 1. Therefore 100% = 100 so x = 100.
14	**7.42am**	2.12pm is 6 hours and 30 minutes after 7.42am.
15	**3300ml**	1l = 1000ml. Change all units to ml, giving 2520ml + 780ml = 3300ml.
16	**22**	As there are only black and white marbles in the box and there is a $^{7}/_{9}$ chance that the marble is black, there is a $^{2}/_{9}$ chance that the marble is white. $^{2}/_{9}$ × 99 = 22.
17	**2**	A rhombus has two lines of symmetry.
18	$^{1}/_{4}$	From the deck of cards, 13 of which are clubs, there is a $^{13}/_{52}$ chance of picking a club at random. This can be simplified to $^{1}/_{4}$ by dividing through by 13.
19	**2**	The highest common factor (HCF) of 26 and 42 is 2.
20	**3**	Rotational symmetry is when a shape is rotated but still seems to have the same original position. An equilateral triangle has a rotational symmetry of order 3. This is because when an equilateral triangle is rotated through 360°, it takes the shape of its original position 3 times.

BLANK PAGE